VISUAL TOPOLOGY

Visual Topology

W. LIETZMANN

Professor of Mathematics, University of Göttingen

TRANSLATED FROM THE GERMAN BY

M. BRUCKHEIMER, Ph.D.

Northampton College of Advanced Technology

1965

CHATTO & WINDUS

LONDON

Published by
Chatto and Windus Ltd
40–42 William IV Street
London W.C.2
★
Clarke, Irwin & Co. Ltd
Toronto

8 25481

The original edition appeared under the title
Anschauliche Topologie
published by Verlag R. Oldenbourg, Munich
© 1955 by R. Oldenbourg, Munich

Printed in Great Britain by
Richard Clay (The Chaucer Press), Ltd., Bungay, Suffolk

Translator's Preface

TOPOLOGY, AS the author remarks in his postscript, is a subject which has advanced by strides since the turn of the century, but until very recently there have been no readable introductory books on the subject in English. It is the aim of the present work to provide such an introduction for the beginner.

It is perhaps a little unfortunate that the first chapter should be the one that will probably be found the least readable, but one might well leave it to the end, or at least reread it then. The rest of the first part of the book deals with the many examples of structures which are made up of physical points and lines. Here the author shows the extent of the subject by including not only amusements, but also technical examples from chemistry, electrical theory, etc., where certain branches of topology are now often applied. He also introduces the terminology of the subject and some simple results.

In the second part of the book the author discusses the topology of surfaces and proves a number of elegant results entirely by elementary means. It should be noted in this connection, that some of the terminology which may appear to have been introduced for no good reason in Part I proves useful in the second part.

It is very often thought that topology is a sort of rubber-sheet geometry. This is not entirely true if we restrict the concept to our three-dimensional imagination. A box within a box is topologically equivalent to two entirely separate boxes, although it is not possible to deform one structure into the other without cutting and rejoining. Our imagination may be restricted by dimension, mathematical continuity is not. This is even better illustrated by going down one dimension. A square within a square and two separate squares (made of wire, say) cannot be deformed into each other on the surface of the table, but there is nothing to stop one lifting them up.

Those remarks of the author which would not have been meaningful in English have been omitted. With these few exceptions, I have tried to render the author's text faithfully, correcting the few minor misprints where they occurred. The majority of references to German papers and works have also been omitted, since most of them are not readily accessible to the reader. I have occasionally added explanatory notes and given references; these are always prefixed by the letters '*Tr*'.

My thanks are due to D. E. Mansfield for reading and correcting many errors in my translation, and to my wife for doing the thankless job of producing a typescript from my illegible manuscript.

March 1964   M. BRUCKHEIMER

Contents

Translator's Preface   v

Author's Preface   xi

PART 1: The Topology of Line-structures

CHAPTER I: Introduction   3

1. *Topology in the framework of the Erlangen Programme*   3
2. *Abstract geometry and the objects of the material world*   7
3. *The topology of concrete objects*   9
4. *Deductive axiomatic and visual methods*   10

CHAPTER 2: Problems of representation   12

1. *Threads*   12
2. *Representation in the plane. Crossings*   12
3. *Line-figures*   14

CHAPTER 3: A single, open thread   16

1. *About the ends of a thread*   16
2. *Meshes and loops*   17
3. *Twists*   18
4. *Crocheting and knitting*   19
5. *Sewing, Bows*   21
6. *Mazes*   22
7. *Friction*   25

CHAPTER 4: Several open threads   27

1. *The joining of two threads*   27
2. *Two-thread seams*   28
3. *Plaiting and weaving*   29
4. *Line-systems or line-complexes*   30
5. *By-passes and fly-overs*   32
6. *Graphs*   33
7. *Trees*   35

8. *Braids*   40

9. *String, rope, cable*   44

CHAPTER 5: A single, closed thread   46

1. *Polygons*   46

2. *Intersections*   46

3. *Knights' tours*   48

4. *Thread games*   49

5. *Knots*   50

6. *The isotopy problem*   53

7. *Wreaths*   56

CHAPTER 6: Line-systems with closed paths   58

1. *Euler's theorem for a polygonal net*   58

2. *Hamilton's dodecahedron game*   59

3. *The Königsberg bridges problem*   60

4. *Unicursal curves*   62

5. *Dominoes*   63

6. *Ferrying*   64

7. *Decanting*   67

8. *Loss of ancestors in a genealogical tree*   68

9. *Mazes again*   69

10. *Multicursal curves*   71

11. *Chains*   72

12. *Linkages*   74

13. *The degree of a graph*   77

14. *Intersection and bridges*   79

15. *Directed graphs*   80

16. *Infinite graphs*   81

PART 2: The Topology of Surfaces

CHAPTER 1: Euler's theorem and the fundamental ideas
of the topology of surfaces   87

1. *Euler's theorem for convex polyhedra*   87

2. *Further proofs of Euler's theorem*   90

3. *Applications of Euler's theorem*   93

4. *Euler's theorem for stacks of polyhedra*   96

5. *Exceptions to the invariant value 1*   98

6. *Boundary, section, connectivity*   103

7. *From polyhedra to curved surfaces*   105

CHAPTER 2: One-sided surfaces   110

1. *The Möbius strip*   110

2. *The heptahedron*   113

3. *The Klein bottle*   116

4. *Orientability*   118

CHAPTER 3: Contiguous regions   123

1. *The 'neighbouring states' theorem*   123

2. *Some extensions of the 'neighbouring states' theorem* 125

3. *The five-colour theorem*   128

4. *The four-colour problem and chromatic numbers*   133

5. *The frontier colour problem*   137

CHAPTER 4: Planes   140

1. *Tiling in the Euclidean plane*   140

2. *The projective plane*   143

3. *The projective plane as a one-sided surface*   145

4. *Finite models of the projective plane*   149

5. *The Boy surface*   151

CHAPTER 5: Riemann surfaces   154

1. *Mapping by linear functions*   154

2. *Riemann surfaces*   157

3. *A Riemann surface of higher connectivity*   161

4. *The slit-open sphere of two sheets*   165

Postscript   168

Bibliography   169

Author's Preface

IN THE volume on geometry in his *Elementary Mathematics from an Advanced Standpoint*, F. KLEIN wrote about Topology: 'It would be highly desirable to have an easily readable account, accessible to the beginner, which by simple examples introduced and developed the general ideas of the abstract theory.'

What was true then ought still to be valid today. Therefore, I gave a course of lectures at Göttingen University, in which the visual concepts of topology were emphasised. I also included this discussion in my teaching lectures, since some of the topics touched upon are mentioned in class—from the first year through to the classes and study groups in the sixth-form. Many of the problems have also for a long time been included in mathematical recreations.

I hope, therefore, that my presentation will be welcomed by both the professional and the amateur mathematician.

W. LIETZMANN

PART 1

The Topology of
Line-structures

CHAPTER 1

Introduction

1. Topology in the Framework of the Erlangen Programme

ELEMENTARY GEOMETRY is usually a metric geometry. Such a geometry is governed by the concept of congruence; the basic axioms deal with the congruence of line-segments, angles and triangles. The geometric structures are considered independent of their position; theorems about the square or the circle do not depend on where these figures lie in the plane or in space. If we restrict ourselves to plane geometry, then propositions are independent of translations and rotations in the plane; the square always remains the same square, the circle the same circle.

This independence can be expressed in analytic form as follows. The equations in terms of co-ordinates, which express the relation between the measures of lines, angles or areas of the respective structures, are invariant under the translations

$$x = x' - a, \quad y = y' - b,$$

where a and b give the translations in the direction of the two axes, and invariant also under the rotations

$$x = x' \cos \theta - y' \sin \theta, \quad y = x' \sin \theta + y' \cos \theta,$$

where θ denotes the angle of rotation about the origin of co-ordinates.

Still in the plane, one can extend the allowable transformations of the geometrical structures by admitting the more general transformation equations

$$x = a_1 x' + b_1 y' + c_1, \quad y = a_2 x' + b_2 y' + c_2,$$

where a_1, a_2, b_1, b_2, c_1, c_2 are real numbers satisfying one more condition, which does not interest us here. The characteristic transformation equations of metric geometry are clearly special cases of these. This geometry is called affine, and in general, the measures of length, angle and area are no longer preserved. Squares may become parallelograms and circles ellipses. What then remains invariant in affine geometry? Even if the length of a line alters, the points of a line still divide the same line-segments; also parallel lines remain parallel and finite structures remain finite. There is a simple mapping

3

process for the transformation of one figure into another to which it is equivalent in affine geometry. It is used, for example, in oblique projection.

Projective geometry goes one step further. Parallelism and the relation of points to line-segments are no longer invariant properties and the exceptional position of the infinite is removed. The square can become an arbitrary quadrilateral, in which not only the length of the sides but also their parallelism is altered. A circle can become, in general, one of the conic sections. The allowable geometric changes can be interpreted as a chain of perspective mappings.

Still restricted to the plane, the analytic expression for a projective co-ordinate transformation is given by the equations[1]

$$x = \frac{a_1 x' + b_1 y' + c_1}{a_3 x' + b_3 y' + c_3}, \quad y = \frac{a_2 x' + b_2 y' + c_2}{a_3 x' + b_3 y' + c_3}.$$

What remains invariant in projective geometry? The cross-ratio

$$(ABCD) = \frac{CA}{CB} : \frac{DA}{DB},$$

where A, B, C, D are points on a straight line, is an invariant.

What we have so far explained is, very briefly, the content of the so-called Erlangen Programme, which FELIX KLEIN formulated[2] in order to establish a system for geometry. The content of metric, affine and projective geometry is the study of those properties of geometric structures which are invariant in each.

Before going one step further, in addition to the concept of invariance under certain transformation equations or mappings, we introduce another general idea. If we have a set of elements (for instance numbers or geometric figures) and also operations on these elements (for instance certain arithmetical operations or mappings) then these operations form a group[3] if the following four conditions are satisfied:

---

[1] Here also $a_1, a_2, a_3, \ldots, c_3$ are real numbers, which must satisfy one further condition which we have not mentioned.

[2] It is true that topology or 'Analysis Situs' is only mentioned in passing in the Erlangen Programme: 'In the so-called analysis situs one looks for the invariants under transformations made up of infinitely small deformations.'

[3] *Tr.* The example given by the author might seem a little confusing to those who are not used to the idea of a group. An ordinary group (in contrast to a group of operations) is a set S of elements $a, b, c, \ldots$ with a law of combination (denoted by o) for which the following four properties hold.
   1. $a \circ b$ belongs to the set S for all a and b of S.

1. Two operations on the elements of the set performed consecutively can be replaced by a single operation.

2. Every operation has an inverse operation.

3. An identity operation exists.

4. The operations are associative.

For instance, take positive and negative numbers as elements and additions as operations, then the additions form a group. For example, $3 + 4 = 7$ and $7 + 5 = 12$ can be replaced by $3 + 9 = 12$, and $3 + 9 = 12$ can be reversed by $12 + (-9) = 3$; $+0$ is the identity operation, and addition is associative, e.g. $(3 + 4) + 5 = 3 + (4 + 5)$. If, however, we had chosen only the positive numbers, then the operations of addition would not form a group.

A characteristic property of the three geometries which we have discussed is that the associated mappings or transformations of each determine a set of operations which form a group. Two translations or two rotations performed consecutively on (plane) figures can be replaced by a single translation or rotation, and each translation or rotation can be reversed by another. This group, which is characteristic of metric geometry, is called the group of displacements.

The affine image of an affine image of a figure can be obtained by a single affine map, and the affine image of a figure can be transformed back to the original by an affine map. These maps also form a group. Corresponding to this affine group there is the projective group for projective geometry. The identity element in each of the three cases

---

2. The associative law holds for o, i.e.

$$(a \text{ o } b) \text{ o } c = a \text{ o } (b \text{ o } c).$$

3. There exists an identity element e such that

$$e \text{ o } a = a \text{ o } e = a \text{ for all } a \text{ of S.}$$

4. For each a of S there is an a' in S with the property that $a' \text{ o } a = a \text{ o } a' = e$.
   a' is called the inverse of a.

With this definition the integers and addition are a group, the integers and multiplication are not.

On the other hand, a set of operations O which operate on another set of elements E (i.e. if g belongs to O and e to E, then $g(e)$ is another element of E) form a group under the conditions stated by the author. Here it is not necessary to specify a law of combination since the combination of two operations of O is always taken to mean their successive application to E. In the author's example E is the set of positive and negative integers and O is the set of operations of addition by integers. Thus $3 + 4 = 7$ means 3 operated on by 4 is 7, and $12 + (-9) = 3$ means 12 operated on by -9 is 3. The distinction in this example between the two approaches is laboured, but when we consider geometries O becomes a given group of transformations and E is the set of geometric objects.

B

is the map which leaves a figure unaffected. Also, in all three cases the associative law is valid.[1]

Just as the group property can be verified for the actual mappings, so it can also be verified for the corresponding transformation equations.

Clearly, not all sets of mappings have the group property. Reflections in lines in the plane do not, for example, form a group, since, in general, two successive reflections cannot be replaced by a single one.

One could now ask whether there are any geometries for which the group property holds, other than those already named. This question would be answered in the affirmative by giving suitable transformation equations. We restrict ourselves to considering a very general transformation, imposing the single condition that it is to be continuous. This will become clearer in the further exposition, but we will immediately make it a little more precise; arbitrary deformations of curves, surfaces and figures are allowed as long as connectivity is maintained. Therefore, distortion, bending, battering, etc., is allowed, but tearing, cutting,[2] breaking, joining or sticking together, welding, cementing, disregarding of holes, etc., is forbidden. In this type of geometry square and circle, cuboid and sphere are equivalent. This topic of geometry is called topology; an earlier name for it was analysis situs.

Topology, therefore, may be regarded as the geometry of properties which remain invariant under topological mappings, that is, under mappings which are such that they and their inverses are one-valued and continuous. In the terms of analytic geometry, these maps are expressed by continuous functions.

Topological maps also have the group character. The object of topology is the establishment of all properties of spatial structures which are invariant under the group of all continuous transformations of space.

Topology is the object of our investigation and, therefore, the concept of this branch of mathematics, its content and its extent, will be gradually consolidated during the course of the exposition.

The approach which has been described here might cause one to

---

[1] *Tr.* For details of these geometries and their characteristic groups see COXETER, *Introduction to Geometry* (Wiley), 1962, and YAGLOM, *Geometric Transformations* (Random House).   For a summary see MANSFIELD and BRUCK-HEIMER, *Background to Set and Group Theory* (Chatto and Windus).

[2] *Tr.* Under certain circumstances we make cuts but join them up again as they were before: e.g. one could in this way remove a box from within a box (see Translator's Preface).

fear that we are dealing with a highly abstract theory. In the majority of books about a strictly mathematical theory of topology, this view is confirmed to a certain extent.

We will instead develop a second approach to the topic. We shall be dealing with concrete, visual and tangible objects. This means, however, that our entry into certain parts of topology is barred, in so far as it concerns itself with objects in n-dimensional space, for example, or brings in the infinite;[1] also, in the methods of topology, we shall dispense with rigorous analytic derivation of facts and prefer visual and experimental methods.

So I hope that anyone who has found the previous discussion somewhat incomprehensible, will not be put off. For a thorough knowledge of topology, abstract methods are, of course, essential, but even for this the present exposition will be found a useful preparation. One of its purposes is exactly that; to smooth the path to topological problems and to topological investigations.

2. *Abstract Geometry and the Objects of the Material World*

When we are concerned with the application of metric geometry to concrete objects in the world which our senses show us, then there is a basic difficulty. An applied metric means that we can put numbers to the service of geometry. But there is an obstacle here which the Greek mathematicians found long ago: metric geometry soon comes to the well-known theorem of PYTHAGORAS; it can be found, for instance, at the end of the first book of EUCLID's *Elements*. This theorem has, as one of its consequences, that in a square whose side is of length 1, the diagonal cannot be represented by a fraction or, as we say, a rational number. Side and diagonal are 'incommensurable'. We write the length of the diagonal as $\sqrt{2}$ and can easily prove that it is not a rational but an irrational number, which as a decimal is, therefore, non-terminating and not periodic.[2] If, however, we actually measure the diagonal of such a unit square made of paper or tin, then the measurement gives a rational value; it makes no

---

[1] We reserve the right to remove this limitation at the end.

[2] Since if $\sqrt{2}$ were a fraction $\frac{m}{n}$ in its lowest terms, that is m and n have no common factor, it would follow from the definition of the square root that $2 = \frac{m^2}{n^2}$ or $2n^2 = m^2$. Thus m would have to be an even number, let us say $2m'$. If in $2n^2 = 4(m')^2$ the factor 2 is removed, then $n^2 = 2(m')^2$, whence n must also be even. But that m and n should both be even contradicts our hypothesis that they have no common factor.

difference whether we measure to a metre, a millimetre, a micron or even more accurately. This property is intrinsic to all measurements.

This discrepancy between geometry and concrete reality appears in the foundations of geometry. A congruence relation satisfies the transitive property which states that if two quantities are equal to a third, then they are equal to each other, as can be found in all elementary text-books. If instead of 'equals' we read 'congruent', this property should also hold for the congruence of line-segments. But in reality, if we measure two pieces of string or wire or two lines a and b, then we can only say that their lengths are equal to within a δ where the δ depends on the measure and the skill of the measurer. Besides, in some circumstances the environment has some effect; for example, for a string we may need to take into account temperature, air pressure, humidity, torsion and perhaps a lot more. Thus it would seem difficult to speak of length at all if we do not mention all such environmental influences as well. Think of the difficulty of fixing the original metre more or less exactly using a metal bar, a difficulty which is fundamentally unaltered if one transfers the problem of determining lengths to the field of optics, to spectroscopy.

So mathematically a does not equal b, but

$$|a - b| < \delta,$$

where δ may be very small, but is nevertheless a finite quantity. Similarly, the equality of the line-segments b and c, which has been determined by measurement, implies

$$|b - c| < \delta.$$

But from these two inequalities we can only conclude

$$|a - c| < 2\delta,$$

which tells us that we may well be able to determine by measurement the inequality of a and c. Thus the transitive law does not hold in real life.

In the natural sciences no one worried about this contradiction for a long time, even if, for example, the surveyor knew that however precise his measurement, he could not obtain exactly 180° for the sum of the angles of a triangle as Euclidean metric geometry predicts. GAUSS, for instance, found that in the triangle formed by Hoher Hagen–Brocken–Inselberg, the sum of the angles was 9·56″ less than 180°. The first to make a detailed study of this problem and to distinguish between 'precise' and 'approximate' mathematics, was FELIX

KLEIN. Later, HJELMSLEV, in particular, tried to establish a natural geometry.

To think that all measuring instruments can be arbitrarily refined is deceptive. Quantum theory proposes that energy is not infinitely divisible, and the Heisenberg uncertainty principle points out the uncertainties in all types of measurement. No one is going to guarantee that one day the quantisation of space and time will not also be taken for granted; the necessity of reasoning in this way should lead to no contradiction.

In these circumstances it is apposite to ask whether anything can be saved of geometry, if we do not regard points as dimensionless, lines as one-dimensional or surfaces as two dimensional, but admit them as the real objects of our senses. What is the geometry of such objects?

3. *The Topology of Concrete Objects*

Thus, in the following exposition, we shall deal with physically perceptible points, lines and surfaces, even if lines, polygons, circles, planes and spheres of the usual geometry do sometimes also appear in the text. We shall, for instance, deal with wires and their extremities, with threads used for sewing, knitting or crocheting, in which knots occur; they will be made into braids, wreaths, chains or nets. We shall discuss roads whose end points are church towers or even whole cities; we shall talk about trees which are made up of twigs, branches and roots, or family trees which are composed of single lines.

Our surfaces will be paper, or cloth which can be made into clothing, or the coloured representation of countries on maps or on the globe, or even counties within a given state. The rings will be tangible, such as a ring made of iron or wood, or, for all I care, a smoke ring or the rings of Saturn, which have no fixed structure and which must first have structure attributed to them. The bodies can be the cake-mould of the baker and his pretzels, or the cast-iron grating of a radiator or a tin sieve with its holes.

Naturally all these objects must be finitely situated since the infinite is not an object of our sense perception. That the two rails of a railway track stretch to infinity and yet do not intersect, i.e. that they are parallel, I can well imagine but I cannot perceive it. Therefore, beside the metric, whether in the Euclidean or non-Euclidean sense, the idea of parallelism has also to be dispensed with.

We shall also consider a finite number of figures such as threads, roads, surfaces, bodies, knots, intersections and holes. The transition to an infinite number of objects would sometimes not be very difficult, but would lead us away from the concrete and will, therefore, at first be avoided.

Nevertheless, the mathematician who likes to remain within the framework of his usual world may take as models of the threads, roads, etc., plane or spatial curves, mathematical surfaces or bodies, regarding them, so to speak, as the mathematical souls of the physical objects. Such a *quid pro quo* between abstract and concrete figures is after all not so strange to him, since in his investigations he uses figures which are drawn on paper with graphite or ink or printer's black, or on a blackboard with coloured chalks where possible, but always drawn as physical figures. He may even not scorn the use of spatial models of wire, cardboard, wood, plaster, etc.

We have seen that such a project cannot be accomplished in metric geometry; in affine or projective geometry it is also impossible. But it works in topology; at least, in certain parts of this branch of knowledge. The description of problems which can be approached in this way is our object for the time being.

4. *Deductive Axiomatic and Visual Methods*

Before we begin we shall say something briefly about the method we shall employ to establish the geometric facts of topology. Strict proofs in mathematics need well-defined axioms and logically deduced theorems. One periodically refers to earlier concepts and theorems, and one has at the beginning a set of basic principles from which an axiomatic system is erected.

One could well do this here where one is dealing with objects of the senses. It would be necessary to modify in a suitable way the axioms of connection and order in the well-known axiomatic system of HILBERT, in order to satisfy the requirement of continuity. Clearly one would not only have to take into account the spatial consistency of the basic geometrical elements, but also the mutual consistencies of lines, curves and plane surfaces.

Instead of building up from a point to a line, to a surface, to a solid, another way would be to reverse the process; to start with a (finite) body, and then to introduce the surface as the boundary or section of a body, the line as the boundary or section of a surface, the points as the boundary or section of a line.

We do not, however, introduce these concepts in their full rigour, because this would not lie within the framework of the exercise which we have set ourselves. We shall use logic, as we do in every science, but we shall prefer inspection and experiment to rigorous deduction. Precisely in this method of approach we have the essential characteristic of our way of presenting the subject matter. Besides, the pure mathematician often uses inspection, otherwise his way of transmitting mathematical facts would sometimes be a very boring business.[1]

We shall use arithmetic as well. The integers with their usual laws of combination will be sufficient; in any case we shall not go beyond the field of rational numbers. Combinatorial theory falls within these limits. This is all the more satisfactory, since these operations can be performed with concrete objects instead of abstract numbers.

[1] For instance, DEHN and HEEGARD write in their article in the large German encyclopaedia of mathematics: 'Analysis situs (= topology) is thus the most primitive part of geometry, where the concept of limit is yet of no importance.' And also: 'Whilst the theory of continuous transformations of space, which is often emphasised, fulfils essentially a dogmatic purpose only . . . inspection is not only the yardstick for the significance of individual results, but it is the best guide for the discovery of new theorems and their proofs.'

CHAPTER 2

Problems of Representation

---

1. *Threads*

IN THIS chapter when we talk of the geometry of a thread or threads, the thread could be replaced by a number of other concrete objects such as string or rope or elastic band. In fact, the objects could be lines made of any sort of material, wires, cables, ribbons, etc., or also roads, river channels, boundaries between countries and many more such things. The important thing is that the extension of these objects is stressed, that in spite of their physical structure we regard the objects as linear, for then it is always possible to represent them as threads. Since we are only interested in relations of connectivity we can reduce the dimensions of the cross-section (although we cannot reduce them to zero). Thus the representation of the structures we wish to examine is a thread situated in three-dimensional space. Geometrically we can approximate the thread by a cylinder with circular cross-section. If knots or intersections or such-like structures are of interest in the investigation, we must be careful to show the structures on the cylinder. However, the means by which the two ends of a thread may be joined together, even if it is a knot, is usually of no interest and can be considered to belong to the inside of the cylinder. Such a structure can be reproduced physically by a hose or elastic band, or in many cases by wire.

2. *Representation in the Plane. Crossings*

We now take a further step in the representation of a thread structure by projecting it into the plane. The thread will then appear as a line of a certain width. Care must be taken to choose the centre of projection (or direction of projection in a parallel projection) so that at any crossing only two threads are involved. This can always be arranged since we are only dealing with a finite number of crossings. The representation is so chosen that the line representing the upper thread is continuous, while the line representing the lower thread is broken; the representation is then said to be 'normed'. Thus, in Fig. 1 *a*, 1 represents the upper, 2 the lower thread.

If three or more threads happen to cross at the same point, then by

12

a suitable displacement the representation can be turned into a set of crossings, each of which only involves two threads. Of the three threads in Fig. 1 *b*, one is certainly at the bottom; let it be thread 1. Pull this one aside and so obtain the situation of Fig. 1 *c*, where it is supposed that thread 2 crosses over thread 3. A representation in which only two threads cross at any one point is called 'regular'.

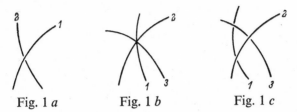

Fig. 1 *a*　　　　　Fig. 1 *b*　　　　　Fig. 1 *c*

If four crossing threads project into lines which intersect at one point, then again one of the threads must be on top. Push that one aside and treat the three remaining threads exactly as before. How many simple crossings have now been obtained? It is evident that this process can be extended to an arbitrary number of crossings. We denote this operation in the geometry of threads by O_0.

In art (for instance in the Viking period) intertwined ribbons were often used as ornaments, and there over- and under-crossing ribbons were similarly distinguished. I have a picture of Shakespeare's Knot Garden in Stratford-on-Avon in front of me, in which narrow flower-beds are used to represent knots in this way.[1]

---

[1] What has SHAKESPEARE to do with knots? I do not know. Is this a mistake or more likely a confusion with mazes? He mentions mazes a number of times. In *A Midsummer Night's Dream* (Act II, Scene 1):

> And the quaint mazes in the wanton green
> For lack of tread are undistinguishable,

and in *The Tempest* (Act III, Scene 3):

> By'r lakin, I can go no further, Sir;
> My old bones ache: here's a maze trod indeed
> Through forthright and meanders!

Tr. There is, of course, no confusion with mazes. The author was unaware of the unusual meaning of the English word knot, that is meaning an elaborately designed flower-bed. Shakespeare uses the word in this sense in, for instance, *King Richard II* (Act III, Scene 4):

> When our sea-walled garden, the whole land,
> Is full of weeds, her fairest flowers choked up,
> Her knots disorder'd and her wholesome herbs
> Swarming with caterpillars.

3. Line-figures

For some purposes it is useful to go one step further in the process of deformation—another deformation which makes no difference to the topological properties of the structure. One can replace the curves which represent the threads in the plane by straight segments, without changing the connectivity, the crossings, etc. Because of our assumptions a finite number of line-segments is always sufficient. One can, for example, replace a simple closed circle by an n-gon, in particular a triangle.

We have here a noteworthy topological invariant. Suppose that an open thread is replaced by a path of k segments, then it is clear that we obtain $e = k + 1$ end-points of these segments; a fact which would also be proved by mathematical induction. Thus

$$I = e - k = 1$$

is an invariant. If the thread is closed, then the corresponding path of line-segments has the invariant

$$I = e - k = 0.$$

As an example of a simple open path, we mention the picture obtained by sketching the Brownian motion of a particle, observed under a microscope.[1] The observer notes the positions of the particle after equal time intervals and when these points are joined up by straight lines a polygonal path is obtained. Naturally, it is fair to suppose that between any two points there is really also a polygonal path and not a straight line, but, since we are dealing with molecular processes, it follows from the finiteness of the number of molecules that the number of lines will remain finite, even with more refined methods of observation.

As an example of an open, branched thread-complex we can take a river with its tributaries (Fig. 2). We have immediately transferred from the actual river to the way it might be represented on a map. Topologically it makes no difference if we represent the sources of the streams and the mouth of the river by points (we shall later call these points end-points) and likewise the places where the smaller streams run into the larger rivers, and if we replace the river channels between such points by line-segments (Fig. 3). Moreover, we do not

[1] The process, discovered in 1827 by the English botanist BROWN, can be observed by using a diluted solution of Indian ink. For a Brownian polygonal path see, for example, G. GAMOW, *Biography of Physics*, p. 115 (Hutchinson), 1962.

even need to reproduce the distance between the points to scale. A representation in which all line-segments are chosen to be equal is topologically equivalent to the map of Fig. 2. TIETZE once showed the practical significance of such a topological distortion by comparing a map of the Munich tram system to a plan of the city.

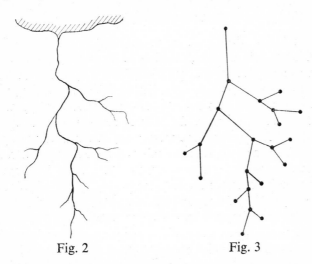

Fig. 2   Fig. 3

It is necessary to make one remark about a closed line path. For a plane polygon we have the condition $e \geqslant 3$. If we remember, however, that the closed line path represents an aggregate of points and lines between these points, then we can also consider two-vertex and one-vertex figures. Neither cause us any trouble, and for these also we have $I = 0$. But a no-vertex figure such as a circle is different. Since there is no point which may be considered a vertex, e is zero and $k = 1$, and so $I = -1$. If we want to maintain the invariant $I = 0$, then we must 'point' any closed line belonging to the topological type of the circle, that is we must provide it with a point. Then if we transfer from a circle to an n-gon, which is after all allowed topologically, the invariant is preserved.

CHAPTER 3

A Single, Open Thread

---

1. *About the Ends of a Thread*

WHEN I TIE a scarf round my throat, when a small girl binds a ribbon in her hair, when I tie the lace of my shoe, in all these cases and in many others we are dealing with single open threads (in our terms) both ends of which are accessible. If we are dealing with a 'bow', then we need only pull the ends and the bow disappears.

In other cases, however, the ends of the thread are not at our immediate disposal. Suppose a woman buys a 'skein' of wool, passes it over a friend's hands or failing this over the back of a chair, takes one end of the woollen thread and winds it into a ball. Then once she begins to knit both ends become inaccessible; the one end is in the middle of the ball of wool and the other is in the knitting. Only if she were to cut a length from the ball for darning, or from a reel of thread to sew, is the first case of a two-ended thread again obtained.

Similarly, the rope which the sailor uses is fixed somewhere at one or both ends, and therefore he cannot make free use of the ends. The same is true of wire, when for example an electric overhead line or a cable is laid. Seen through the eyes of the mathematician, these cases correspond to the assumption that the thread goes to infinity at both ends.

Consider a Quipu, the cord used by the primitive inhabitants of South America for counting. From one cross-thread hang many vertical threads: select one of these threads. In it are knots, whose form is at the moment of no interest. But to make these knots in the string, the Indian had to have access to the free end; the other end, which was fixed to the cross-thread, was of no use to him. Mathematically, we can express this by saying that we are dealing with a thread one end of which goes to infinity and whose other end is finitely situated.

We will not examine whether one can always reduce the case of a thread with two free ends to that with one end free. One could tie a bow-tie, or more simply a scarf, round one's neck by manipulating one end only (a man with one hand amputated is, after all, forced to do so); the other could be held by someone during the whole process. Naturally, it is more convenient to use both ends.

16

2. *Meshes and Loops*

We shall now consider a thread with both ends inaccessible and investigate some of the 'twists' which can be made in it, which, as we shall see, are of great practical importance.

We have two basic forms, the 'mesh' and the 'loop'. Fig. 4 shows the mesh and Fig. 5 the loop, which the sailor calls a half-hitch.[1] The mesh, which can easily be made with a thread or a piece of wire (on the road one would call it a hairpin bend) is characterised by a change of direction, but without the crossing and rotation shown by the loop (consider the Gotthard railway tunnel). Regarded as a curve,

Fig. 4   Fig. 5

the mesh has inflectional tangents, and the centre of curvature changes sides of the curve, which need not be so for the loop. A loop can be obtained from a mesh by taking its upper end and rotating it through 180°. With the opposite rotation one can change a loop into a mesh and thus remove the crossing. This is a first basic operation; to remove or produce a crossing; we shall call it O_1.

In a piece of string, both of whose ends are inaccessible, make two loops, which are symmetric to each other, that is in both crossings the same piece of thread is uppermost (Fig. 6 *a*). This position of the thread can be obtained by taking the upper end (the head) of the mesh and placing it over the lower part (the feet). If one now rotates the right loop backwards through 180°, so that it is covered by the left loop, and puts a stick through the loopholes, one obtains the handle often used for carrying a parcel tied with string.

If two similar loops are put (Fig. 6 *b*) together so that one covers the other, another adaptation for a carrying handle is obtained (in Fig. 7, in order to show the way this is obtained, the loops cover each

---

[1] I quote from a sailors' manual: 'Characteristic of seamen's knots (in our terminology they are mostly twists) is that they can be made quickly and easily even in total darkness, that the more they are strained the better they hold, and that one can undo them easily. In their making, the turns and knots must be well pulled through, and one must always work with sufficiently long ends of rope and away from the body. The left hand holds the rope while the right works.'

other partially only). The handle is put through the common opening. Sailors call this double loop a clove-hitch and use it when mooring a

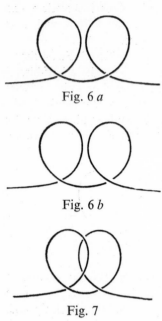

Fig. 6 *a*

Fig. 6 *b*

Fig. 7

boat by throwing both loops, one after the other, over a bollard on the quay.

In this double loop the number of crossings is increased from two to four, by placing a bit of thread (the right of the left loop) over the other bit of thread (the left of the right loop). By the reverse manipulation the two extra crossings in Fig. 7 can be removed. We shall call this second basic operation, to produce or remove two similar and adjacent crossings, O_2. The double loop of Fig. 6 *a* is produced from a mesh by such an operation O_2.

Of the many other possible twists of a thread both of whose ends are inaccessible, we shall describe two more. The first is obtained by slipping a loop over a mesh, as shown in Fig. 8. Next take a double mesh (on the road it would be a double hairpin), form at each end of the double mesh a loop and

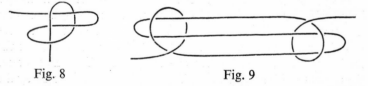

Fig. 8   Fig. 9

slip these over the two heads of the double mesh (Fig. 9). Naturally the loose structure shown in the figure, which arises in the process of construction, must be pulled tight. This sheepshank can be pulled taut at both ends.

3. *Twists*

If a thread has one—or two—accessible ends then a twist, which is commonly called a knot, can be more easily made. Since the mathematician only speaks of a knot when the thread is closed, we will here not speak of a knot when the thread is open, but of a twist—this is contrary to everyday usage. The existence of the free end permits one not only to make such twists, but also the opposite, to undo them again and to restore the untwisted thread.

Fig. 10 shows the usual simple twist, Fig. 11 a somewhat altered 'firmer' twist.

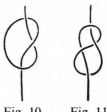

Fig. 10   Fig. 11

The thumb knot, as the sailor calls the twist of Fig. 10, can be repeated many times. It is used, for example, when knotting the end of a piece of string about a parcel, or when the twist is slipped round a stick. In both cases, in order to undo the twist, it is sufficient to withdraw the end of the thread from one loop. The simpler twist shows three, and the other four crossings.

We mentioned above the Quipu used by the ancient inhabitants of South America—a set of ropes in which by certain forms of twists numbers were marked. These twists clearly had some statistical significance. The units were represented by the forms illustrated in Fig. 12. Two different twists representing 1 have become known to us and are shown. The meaning of the forms for 2 to 9 are immediately obvious; the reader can easily reproduce them. One must be careful though, that the cross-threads which denote the numerical value lie close together without crossing. For this purpose it is best to use a rather thick string.

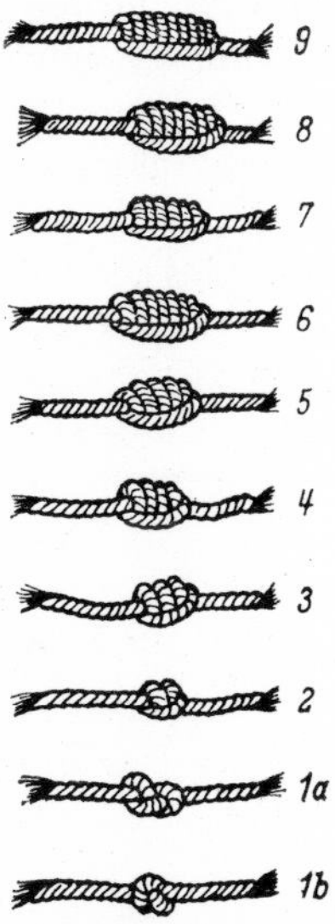

Fig. 12

4. Crocheting and Knitting

Considerably more involved is the threading done in 'crocheting'. The method is represented in principle in Fig. 13. One begins with a loop at one end of the thread (a). With the crotchet-hook a mesh is pulled through the loop (b); through the loop thus created a new mesh is pulled (c) and thus the process is continued (d). This knotless threading, which is of course later pulled together, is shown again in (e). As long as the free end is not fixed, a pull on it will unravel the whole crochet-work.

Simple lace is crocheted, that is made from one thread. We will not here go into the making of bone-lace, that is lace made with a num-

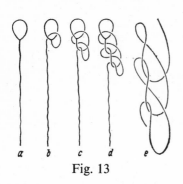

ber of threads. The connoisseur does not know what to admire more, the workmanship or the beauty of the pattern in crocheted and bone-lace.

Knitting is really two-dimensional crocheting. The easiest way of explaining the process involved in knitting is to examine the simple device which children use to knit 'reins'. A hole is bored along the axis of a cork. Four or five pins

a   b   c   d   e

Fig. 13

are stuck round the edge. A thread is looped round the pins and then with the knitting needle a mesh is pulled through the already existing mesh at each of the upright pins (Fig. 14 *a*). In the usual form of

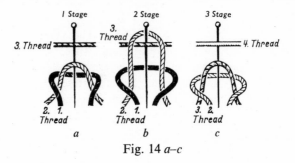

Fig. 14 *a–c*

knitting one uses long knitting needles which serve a double purpose. In the first place they maintain the stitches and thus the needle crosses a row of stitches (Fig. 14 *b*). Secondly the point of the needle draws a further mesh through the already existing meshes (stitches) and produces in time a new row of stitches (Fig. 14 *c*).

Figs. 15 *d* and *e* show two pieces of knitting which have been made in this way. One can pull the new mesh through the old one from the back or the front. In case 15 *d* the method changes from mesh to mesh in each row—one knits 'once from the right and once from the left'. In case 15 *e*, a whole row is knitted from the front, the next from the back, and so on alternately.

If in a piece of knitting a stitch is broken for some reason or other, then the whole column of stitches (a ladder) which hangs on it (Fig.

15 *c*) is affected—one speaks of a stitch having been dropped. Also, in time, more and more of the stitches adjoining the torn stitch, and in the same row, are affected.

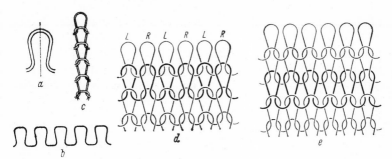

Fig. 15 *a–e*

The knitting process is considerably accelerated by a knitting machine: a fine ladies' stocking with 2 million meshes is made by a machine in less than 10 minutes from a thread 4·8 km long and 0·15 mm thick.

If one were to pull on the free end of the crocheting or knitting thread, then the whole piece of lace or knitting comes undone. This constitutes a significant difference from the twists considered in § 3.

5. *Sewing, Bows*

If the thread is finite in both directions, then sewing is the first thing that comes to mind. A thread is pulled through the eye of a needle, so that (in our terms) a mesh is formed there, and the other end is twisted as in Fig. 10 or 11, so that the end of the thread does not pull

Fig. 16   Fig. 17

through the material at the first stitch. Then stitch follows stitch in such a way that the thread passes alternately on the one or other side of the material (Fig. 16). Beside this simplest form of sewing, which, of course, instead of advancing could be done at one spot—as when sewing on a button—there exist many other sorts of stitches and seams. Thus, for instance, when hemming the edge of a piece of cloth, before proceeding to the next stitch the thread is pulled through the loop made by the previous stitch.

C

A word about those thread structures (laces, ribbons), which one calls 'bows'. In order to give the bow a certain firmness, a simple twist is made (Fig. 17) with the two ends of the bow-tie or the hair-ribbon or the laces sticking out of the last holes of the shoe. Then the bow is bound, usually two-sided—how this is done need not be mentioned since everyone can do it. The result is two free ends and two meshes sticking out of the twisted section. The essential thing is that if one grips the meshes and pulls them apart the twisted section becomes tighter, whereas if one pulls the free ends the bow disappears.

6. *Mazes*

Daedalos built a maze for King Minos on the island of Crete and in the middle sat the Minotaur. Each year Athens had to send a tribute of seven boys and seven girls, who were sent into the maze and became a sacrifice to the monster, till Theseus came, slew the Minotaur and found his way out of the maze alive, thanks to the 'thread of Ariadne'. I suppose that he attached one end of the thread at the entrance and unravelled it from a ball in his pocket until he had fortunately reached the evil inmate in the depths of the maze; having done the deed he rewound the thread slowly back on to the ball.

Fig. 18   Fig. 19

To copy the form of this labyrinth was seemingly a favourite exercise of skill in the ancient world; its likeness can be found on coins (Fig. 18) and also on the walls of houses in cities (Fig. 19), the latter being drawn by a child's hand. It is remarkable that the same design occurs in the North under the name of Trojeborg, on Visby, for instance. Whether these stone settings are contemporary with the designs of the Mediterranean area, or of later origin, has to the best of my knowledge not been settled to date.

The formation of the figure is explained in Fig. 20. The centre is a cross; in each of the four squares there fit lines, which have three ends in the case of the Knossos coins and five in the case of the Trojeborg. In the first case the lines are numbered so that the ends with the same numbers are to be joined without crossing. In the other, more complicated case the reader should carry out the numbering himself. This is how the typical maze pattern is formed, not as a spiral, as I was once told in a lecture by a student of folk-lore.

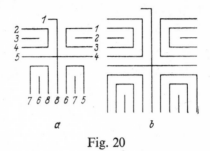

Fig. 20

The difficulty of this **maze** certainly does not lie in trying to go from the outside to the centre and then to find one's way out again; the path is uniquely prescribed and cannot be missed. Thus we would not need Ariadne's thread in this case, since we know the method of construction. But in later times, there occur mazes which are much more complicated in form, embroidered on the ceremonial robes of Christian rulers, or also as ornaments in churches. One of the oldest drawings of this type is a representation of a maze on the church of St. Quentin, of the early 12th century.[1] In more recent times mazes were created by gardeners using hedges or similar things as walls. These became more complicated than the simple basic pattern found in Crete.

As an example take the maze at Hampton Court—reproduced with small changes in Fig. 21. The entrance is marked by an arrow. What method will ensure that the traveller will reach the centre? The following prescription is given: always stick to the right-hand wall (or, of course, to the left-hand wall). It is easily seen that in this way every blind alley is safely negotiated, and in any case one will certainly get out again.

The question remains though, whether in this way one passes along all paths. That being the case, then one certainly has been through the centre. But it need not be the case at all. There can be islands which one does not reach by this method. If the reader draws the path through the Hampton Court maze with a pencil, he will discover two such islands on the left side of the maze. The wanderer

[1] See H. E. DUDENEY, *Amusements in Mathematics*, pp. 127 ff. (Nelson), 1917, who cites many other examples.

must at some stage go from one wall to the one opposite, contrary to his instructions. If he happens to have landed on an island and then goes on following the rule, he will never get off it; he wanders round 'in a circle'. If he eventually notices this and changes wall again in order to get off the island, then he may well, in our maze, land on the other island. Therefore, one must be careful when deviating from the rule. It is now clear then that if the centre, which is the

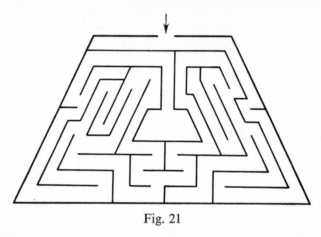

Fig. 21

traveller's goal, lies on such an island, then the rule will not get him there.[1]

The example we chose has only one entrance, but there exist mazes with more than one. Thus it is apparent that the problem of the unique path through the Cretan maze can be made even more complex—and DUDENEY tells of a man in Philadelphia who went mad looking for paths through mazes, and put a bullet through his head. The thread of Ariadne would not have been of much use to him.

If the maze has many entrances, and if one does not come out where one originally entered, one need only regard this exit as closed and wander on, repeating the process until one returns to the original entrance. Nevertheless it is obvious that one does not have the guarantee that in this wandering one has passed through all the paths, and so if one is looking for something—and it need not be just a Minotaur—one may not find it.

I shall leave till later (Chapter 5, § 9) the instructions needed to make sure that all paths are traversed. It is unimportant whether these walks through a maze take place in the plane or in space. The

[1] I have taken as a basis for the drawing the plan given by DUDENEY.

given rule, with its limitations, is appropriate, for example, for wandering through the network of paths in caves, mines, catacombs, etc.

7. Friction

A cable railway covers in steep ascent the 1000m difference in height between valley and mountain in barely 10 minutes. At the top the load of the cable on which the cabin slides is anchored by simply winding the cable a few times round a drum, a few metres in diameter. When a boat is to be arrested at a landing stage a rope is thrown across from it, wound once or twice round a bollard, and the boat comes to rest. How is this possible?

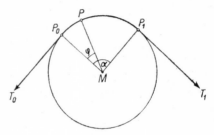

Fig. 22

In Fig. 22, T_0 and T_1 denote the tensions at the ends of a rope which is wound round a fixed (i.e. non-revolving) drum whose centre is the point M. The rope touches the drum between P_0 and P_1; let the angle at the centre, P_0MP_1, be α. Let the tension, which at P_0 has the value T_0, at P_1 the value T_1, have the value T at an arbitrary point P in the piece of rope which is in contact with the drum. Let the corresponding angle at the centre, P_0MP, be ϕ. Suppose that μ is the coefficient of friction, which is dependent on the material of the rope and drum, then[1]

$$\frac{dT}{d\phi} = \mu T.$$

Integrating this differential equation subject to the boundary condition that for $\phi = 0$, $T = T_0$, one obtains

$$\log T - \log T_0 = \mu\phi$$

or

$$\log \frac{T}{T_0} = \mu\phi$$

or

$$T = T_0 e^{\mu\phi}.$$

For $\phi = \alpha$ one obtains

$$T_1 = T_0 e^{\mu\alpha}.$$

This is Euler's formula for a rope.

The coefficient of friction of a hemp rope on wood or iron is of

[1] *Tr.* See Loney, *Statics* (C.U.P.).

the order of 0·5. If it is wound halfway round the drum, i.e. $\alpha = \pi$, $e^{\mu\pi} \approx 5$, therefore $T_1 \approx 5T_0$; for $\alpha = 2\pi$, i.e. wound once completely round, it is found that $T_1 \approx 23T_0$, for twice round $T_1 \approx 535T_0$. Thus T_1 grows very rapidly with the increasing number of turns.

Even with a coefficient of friction $\mu \approx 0·2$ of steel on steel, for which very roughly $e^{\mu\pi} \approx 2$, T_1 grows by powers of 2, that is somewhat slowly at first, but then later very quickly.

The reader should calculate roughly how many times a drum or post on a landing stage must be encircled in order to balance a pull of 10 tons by a pull of 1 kg.

The radius of the drum does not enter into the formula. It does, however, play a part in that the stiffness of the rope must not hinder its application to the drum.

When one or more threads are twisted among themselves, friction also plays a decisive role. It is the cause of our not being able to undo twists which come out to be meshes or loops by a light pull—take for example the two twists in Figs. 8 and 9. If the threads and ropes were mathematical lines and hence frictionless, then it would, for example, be immediately obvious that all knotless twists of a thread with two ends fixed are topologically equivalent. What we mean by knotted, or in contrast by not knotted, will be investigated in Chapter 5.

CHAPTER 4

Several Open Threads

1. *The Joining of Two Threads*

THE SIMPLEST everyday example is of two threads which need joining, and we begin with the case when each of the two has at least one accessible end. We also include the case when one thread with two ends is made into a closed thread by joining the ends—the join is then ignored.

A very firm join which is usually called a knot (although the mathematician restricts the term knot to a twist in a closed thread) is obtained if one lays the two threads next to each other and makes a simple twist with them (Fig. 10). Then one pulls the twist tight and separates the threads (Fig. 23).

Fig. 23

Another common method is to start with a twist of the two threads as shown in Fig. 17. The same twist is performed again with the ends *a* and *b*, and one obtains the twist of Fig. 24 *a* or 24 *b*, depending on whether the second twist is of the

Fig. 24 *a*   Fig. 24 *b*

same kind as the first or different from it. The twist Fig. 24 *a* is known as the reef knot,[1] which is not very popular since it can be diffi-cult to undo. Most unpopular and in fact taboo for sailors is the 'granny' of Fig. 24 *b*, since it cannot be undone again if it is pulled tight. The twist Fig. 25 *a* is known as a sheet bend and is particularly easy to undo. An improvement on the sheet bend with regard to efficiency is the

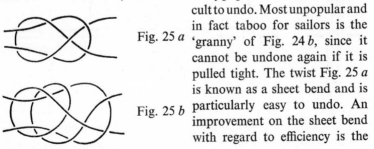

Fig. 25 *a*

Fig. 25 *b*

[1] These knottings are in common use and have various names.

double sheet bend (Fig. 25 *b*). Even if one wishes to attach one thread to another, both of whose ends are inaccessible, these twists are possible by forming a mesh in the second thread and then interlacing the first (see Figs. 24 *a* and 25 *a*).

2. *Two-thread Seams*

When sewing two threads are sometimes used instead of one. For instance, when the cobbler wishes to join two pieces of leather, he makes holes through them with an awl and then pulls two waxed

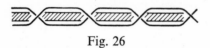

Fig. 26

threads through the holes as in Fig. 26, one from the top and one from the bottom. Sewing machines usually use two threads. One thread is led from a reel through the eye at the tip of the needle, which moves up and down. The other thread is in a horizontal shuttle which moves to and fro under the surface on which the cloth rests. Fig. 27 shows the various stages in the process.

1. The needle N, with the thread T_1, makes a hole in the cloth and carries the thread T_1 down.

2. The needle moves up, but leaves an open mesh of thread T_1 beneath the cloth.

3. The shuttle passes through the mesh and carries the thread T_2 through it.

4. The cloth is pulled forward—to the right in Fig. 27—and the mesh in T_1, through which T_2 passes, is thus drawn tight.

5. The needle is now ready for the next stitch. The shuttle has gone back, but the thread T_2 remains in the mesh, and the process is repeated.

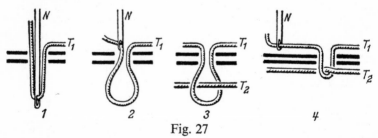

Fig. 27

The sewing machine not only has the advantage of speed, but also the advantage that the seam is firmer, because two interlaced threads have been used.

3. *Plaiting and Weaving*

Fig. 28 shows a commonly used chain-link fencing made of plaited wire. Only wires which run from top to bottom are used. Two neigh-bouring wires may be intertwined simply (as shown in the diagram) or doubly. A woven fabric differs from such a plaited network in that the wires or threads which run up and down are alternately crossed, above and below, by horizontal wires or threads as shown in Fig. 29. A variation of this is the weave called 'gauze' (Fig. 30). Numerous other types of plaiting and weaving differ to a greater or lesser extent from these simplest forms. The forms may also be dependent on the type of material, for example basket canes, the straw used for thatching and the wool of woven carpets.

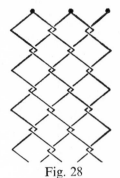

Fig. 28

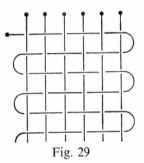

Fig. 29

The simplest form of weaving is per-formed on an old vertically working loom; it was already known in prehistoric times. Perpendicular weighted threads hang close together from a horizontal bar. A thread, the weft, has to be passed horizontally through the hanging threads so that, in the simplest case, alternately one thread is crossed above and the next crossed below. To do this by hand, thread for thread, would be very tiresome. The fact that in the next transit of the weft, over-crossed threads have to be under-crossed and vice versa, makes it even more difficult, and so the mecha-nism depicted in Fig. 31 is used. The vertical threads are numbered and those with odd numbers are fixed by small hooks to a horizontal 'heddle-rod' and can thereby be pulled forward together. The threads with even numbers (dashed

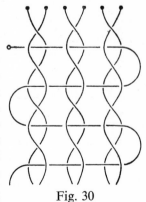

Fig. 30

in the figure) are held in a forward position by a horizontal 'separating-rod'. For the first transit of the weft the odd threads hang vertically; it follows that the weft passes over these threads and under the even ones. Before the weft returns in the opposite direction, the heddle-rod pulls the odd threads forward so that they now cross

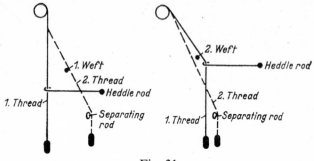

Fig. 31

over the weft, while the even threads pass underneath it. The situation is shown in plan in Fig. 32 *a*. The vertical threads appear as points; the first weft crosses over the second, the next would in turn be crossed by the second, and so on.

There are several variations of weaving patterns; two are illustrated

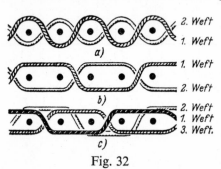

Fig. 32

in Fig. 32 *b* and 32 *c*. In 32 *b* the weft, instead of alternately passing over and under the vertical threads, passes over two and then under two, and so on. The situation is similar for the first and third weft in case *c*, but the second weft is displaced one thread to the right relative to the other two. The weaving depicted in *a* is used for taffeta silk and *b* is called Panama or mat-weaving. The twill *c* shows a characteristic pattern on the surface; in fact all the different types of weaving can be recognised by an expert from the surface of the woven fabric.

4. *Line-systems or Line-complexes*

We examine a connected system of threads, paths or curves. By connected we mean that one can go from any chosen point of the system to any other by way of the threads, paths or curves. Therefore, we exclude systems which are made up of two separate aggregates, for example, two n-gons which lie next to or inside each other, without common points. Topologically we can always replace the threads, paths or curves by straight line-segments, and that is why one discusses line-complexes. Another term for line-complexes is graphs.

Among the points of such a complex there may be end-points, i.e. points from which only one line starts. Let the number of such points be e_1. Then there may be points from which lines start in two directions. Such points can always be removed by replacing the two lines meeting at that point by a single line and dropping the point. But, for any cases in which this reduction is not made, we will denote the number of such points by e_2. In general, we shall denote by e_r the number of points from which r lines start. Then the total e of points of the line-complex is

$$e = e_1 + e_2 + e_3 + \ldots + e_n,$$

where n is the largest number of lines starting from any point of the complex.

The number k of lines can be calculated as follows. If we count each point which has i lines starting from it i times, and note that each line has two end-points, then

$$k = \tfrac{1}{2}(e_1 + 2e_2 + 3e_3 + \ldots + ne_n).$$

The expression in brackets is an even integer, since k is integral.

The line-complex is said to be closed if no end-points exist, i.e. $e_1 = 0$. We shall call it reduced, if also $e_2 = 0$. A convex n-gon is a closed but not reduced line-complex.

In Fig. 3 we had a line-complex which was topologically equivalent to a river basin; there

$$e - k = 1,$$

because there were no lines which could be removed without the line-complex being separated into two line-complexes. Such a line-complex is generally called a tree.

A line is called a bridge if the complex would fall into two, if the line were removed. A complex can be split into at most $s + 1$ complexes by the removal of s lines. In a tree every line which is not an end-line is a bridge. But in some line-complexes one can omit lines without the complex falling apart. Suppose that all such lines are removed. Then there is no closed path in the complex; because if such a closed path existed we could leave out one of its lines and the complex would remain connected. This is shown, for example, by an arbitrary closed polygon.

When all closed paths are excluded, then between e points there are at most $k = e - 1$ lines. We will now consider such line-complexes. In Chapter 5 we shall return to line-complexes with closed paths.

5. By-passes and Fly-overs

A trunk road runs through the town G. In order to free the town of through traffic a diversion is arranged for all vehicles which have no business in the town. This is shown in Fig. 33.

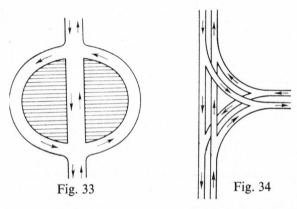

Fig. 33   Fig. 34

When planning the Berlin overhead railway the crossing of the

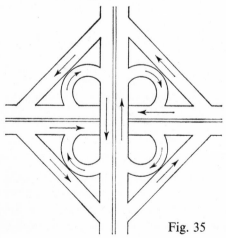

double tracks at the same level was avoided. Fig. 34 shows how such a triangle of tracks could be arranged. Also on the autobahns crossings at the same level are avoided. Fig. 35 shows the approach and run-off roads between two motorways. One may drive in one direction only along the two sides of the motorway, as also on the approach and run-off roads.

Fig. 35

6. Graphs[1]

Suppose we have a number of objects which are isolated from each other. We represent them by points in the plane. In Fig. 36 they are the points 1 to 24. In a graph every point is connected to at least one other point. Thus there must be no isolated points like point 16 in Fig. 36. We will exclude for the time being the case in which the number of points is not finite. (The simplest example of a line-complex with an infinite number of points is the real line with the natural numbers as points.) Nevertheless, even when the number of points is finite, the number of connections could be infinite; there would then be at least one point-pair joined by an infinite number of lines. We shall exclude this case as well, that is

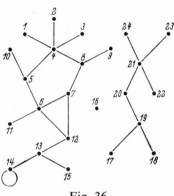

Fig. 36

e, the number of points, and k, the number of connections, are finite. In Fig. 36, $e = 24$, $k = 24$. The railway network of a country, whether in its natural state or drawn on a map, forms an example with a large, but nevertheless finite, number of points and connections.

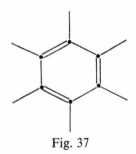

Fig. 37

For the time being we shall impose a further restriction: between any two points there shall be only one connection. Thus, for instance, chemical structures in which there is more than one bond between atoms are excluded. An example of such a structure is the well-known benzene-ring (Fig. 37). However, the switching diagrams of any electrical system belong to our present discussion. For these Kirchhoff's laws hold. Incidentally, the investigations of Kirchhoff were really the first beginnings of a theory of line-complexes or graphs. One is concerned there with

[1] *Tr.* There is now a book in English on the theory of graphs. It is *The Theory of Graphs* by CLAUDE BERGE, translated by ALISON DOIG (Methuen), 1962. This book, although elementary in the technical sense, is more 'mathematical'; the present work should prove a useful introduction. I have tried to use the same technical terms whenever possible.

branch points between which current lines exist. If in a conducting wire k_v, of resistance r_v, there flows a current i_v, and there is a voltage difference e_v between its ends, then Kirchhoff's first law states that at any arbitrary point of the system

$$\Sigma i_v = 0,$$

where the summation is over all electric currents meeting at that point, and where every i_v has the appropriate sign. Kirchhoff's second law states that in every closed loop of the system

$$\Sigma i_v . r_v = \Sigma e_v,$$

summed over all wires of the loop, and where each i_v and e_v is taken signed.

In general we can imagine the connections between the points as straight lines. The number n of lines leaving a point we shall call the degree of the point. The degree of an isolated point would be 0, but we have excluded such points. Points whose degree is 1 we have called end-points: such are, for example, in Fig. 36 the points 1, 2, 3, 9, 10, 11, etc. Lines which start from end-points are called end-lines, e.g. $\overline{1,4}$, $\overline{2,4}$, $\overline{3,4}$, $\overline{9,8}$, $\overline{10,5}$, $\overline{11,6}$, etc.

What has been determined so far is a finite graph. We shall further exclude any line which starts and ends at the same point without passing through any other point, for example, point 14 in Fig. 36. Such a line-complex is called a graph in the restricted sense. A telephone network, in which a subscriber cannot ring himself, is a graph in the restricted sense.

Up till now it has not been assumed that the graph is connected. The river system of a country, where the points and lines are interpreted in the sense of Fig. 3, or a forest with its trunks, branches, twigs, roots, etc., on the distinct trees, do not form connected graphs. The graph of Fig. 36 is not connected. We will call a graph connected if from every point to every other there is at least one path. Even if we restrict the concept of a path to a sequence of connected line-segments each of which is used once only, there will, in general, be a number of paths from any one point to any other. Among these paths from one point to another there will be one or more paths which require the least number of lines. If this is n, then n is called the distance of the points from each other. If one gives each line the length 1, which is often meaningfully possible, then n is the measure of the shortest path. In Fig. 36 the distance from 1 to 7 is 3.

A closed path is to be understood as a path which returns to the starting point, but, of course, not along the same line; that is not from a point A to a neighbouring point B and then from B back to A. A closed path is sometimes called a circle (cycle) since a circle is topologically equivalent to the polygonal path. Examples of closed paths in Fig. 36 are 4, 5, 6, 7, 8, 4 and 6, 12, 7, 6 and 4, 5, 6, 12, 7, 8, 4.

In a finite, connected, cycle-less graph in the restricted sense, there is only one path from one point to any other. We call such a graph a tree. The graph 17, 18, . . . 24 in Fig. 36 is a tree, but not the graph 1, 2, . . . 15.

7. *Trees*

A real tree, regarded as made up of a trunk, branches and twigs, leaves and needles, together with its roots, is topologically equivalent to the line-complex which we have called a tree. Hence the name tree. The flower growth of an umbelliferous plant is another fine example of a topological tree. One, of course, excludes the occasional occurrence of two branches which have grown together.

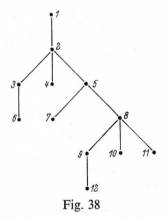

Fig. 38

Genealogical trees are also trees in our sense; for instance, the tree of the well-known Swiss family of mathematicians BERNOULLI reproduced in Fig. 38. I have entered only those members of the family who are needed to show the descent of the known mathematicians among them (e.g. 2 = Nikolaus had 11 children!).

The corresponding key is: 1. Jakob 1598?–1634, 2. Nikolaus 1623–1708, 4. Jakob 1654–1705, 5. Johann 1667–1748, 6. Nikolaus 1687–1759, 7. Daniel 1700–1782, 9. Daniel 1751–1834, 10. Jakob 1759–1789, 11. Johann 1744–1807, 12. Christoph 1782–1863.

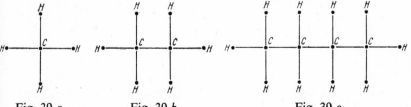

Fig. 39 *a*   Fig. 39 *b*   Fig. 39 *c*

Take the structural formulae of chemistry as a further example. For instance, consider the paraffins, which are characterised by the formula C_nH_{2n+2} then if e is the number of vertices (the number of atoms) and k the number of bonds, we have

when $n = 1$ (i.e. CH_4) $e = 5,$ $k = 4$ (Fig. 39 a):
when $n = 2$ (i.e. C_2H_6) $e = 8,$ $k = 7$ (Fig. 39 b):
and when $n = 4$ (i.e. C_4H_{10}) $e = 14,$ $k = 13$ (Fig. 39 c).
In general $e = 3n + 2,$ $k = 3n + 1.$

Molecules with the same atomic composition but with different properties are said to be isomeric. For instance, Figs. 40 a and 40 b show the two forms of ethylenedicarbonic acid, a is the axially symmetric maleic acid, b is the centrally symmetric fumaric acid; in Figs. 40 c and 40 d we have, corresponding to the first two acids, the axially symmetric *meso*-tartaric acid and the centrally symmetric D-tartaric acid.

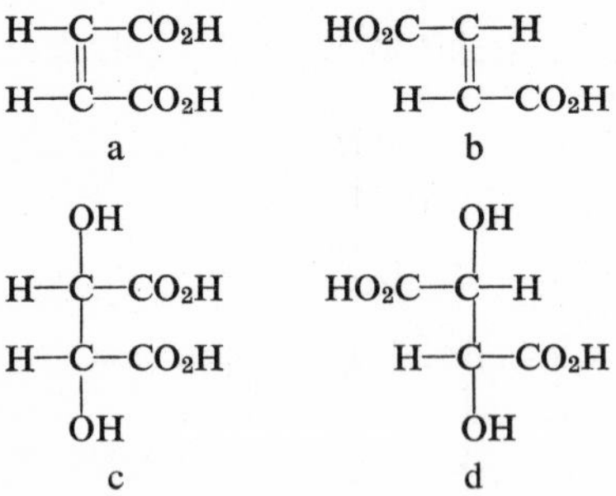

H—C—CO₂H   HO₂C—C—H
‖   ‖
H—C—CO₂H   H—C—CO₂H

a   b

        OH   OH
        | |
H—C—CO₂H   HO₂C—C—H
        | |
H—C—CO₂H   H—C—CO₂H
        | |
        OH   OH

c   d

Fig. 40 a-d

STUDY has shown, by an example, how a discussion of the various possibilities of tree forms with the same number of points can be useful in chemistry. He restricts himself to the paraffins and in

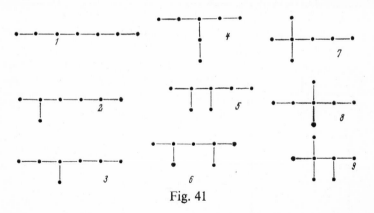

Fig. 41

particular examines the case $n = 7$, the heptanes. The various isomers are characterised by the arrangement of the carbon atoms, that is by the trees with seven points. He lists them in the form reproduced in Fig. 41. The corresponding names of the compounds are:

1. Normal heptane—known,
2. 2-methyl hexane—known,
3. 3-methyl hexane—known in two enantiomorphic forms because of the asymmetrical construction,
4. 3-ethyl pentane—known,
5. 2:3-dimethyl pentane— known in two forms because of the asymmetrical construction,
6. 2:4-dimethl pentane,
7. 2:2-dimethyl pentane— known,
8. 3:3-dimethyl pentane— known,
9. 2:2:3-trimethyl butane.

I have added a little to STUDY by showing which of these theoretically possible compounds are known.

I give below a table, calculated by CAYLEY, showing the number N of theoretically possible paraffins corresponding to different n:

$$n = 1\ 2\ 3\ 4\ 5\ 6\ 7\ \ 8\ \ 9\ 10\ \ 11\ \ \ 12\ \ \ 13$$
$$N = 1\ 1\ 1\ 2\ 3\ 5\ 9\ 18\ 35\ 75\ 159\ 355\ 802.$$

One notices that the number N, that is the number of possible tree forms, increases rapidly with increasing n.

Since we are already discussing chemistry, we will also mention an example of a closed line-complex. I choose the cellulose molecule: alternately asymmetric sugar residues periodically repeating themselves, form long chains (Fig. 42).

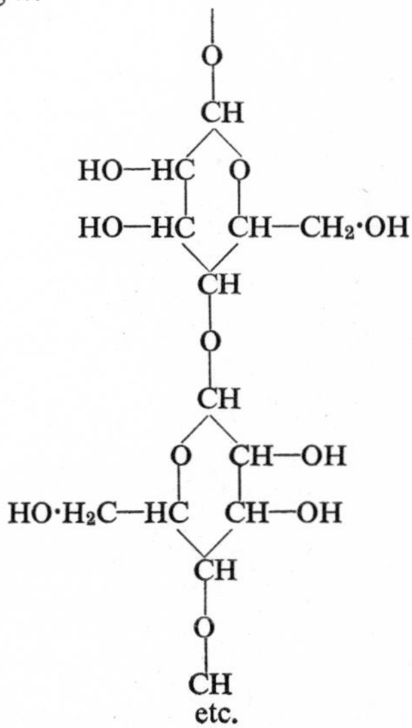

E. STUCKE posed himself 'a mathematical–aesthetical problem' in which he tried to introduce some system into the great number of possible trees. One can construct, for $n = 1, 2, 3, \ldots$ the topologically different trees with $n + 1$ points (or, since $k = e - 1$, with n lines), or one can construct trees with a prescribed number of end-lines. Points from which only two lines start would be omitted since they are immaterial to the structure of the tree. STUCKE has drawn up a table

Fig. 42

D

THE TOPOLOGY OF LINE-STRUCTURES

of the trees without two-fold points with seven end-points using symmetric arrangements where possible. The lines are all made of equal length. Fig. 43 reproduces 15 of his 20 different trees, in a different and certainly less aesthetic form; the other trees drawn by him seem to me not to be topologically different. Except for *f, h, m, n, o*, all are axially symmetric. The reader should try to set up a complete table of trees with three, four, five, six boundary points.

We will now derive some general results about trees. If one removes the end-lines from a tree, then in general a tree remains. The exception is when the original was a star, i.e. a tree which consists of only one point and a number *n* of lines radiating from it. If one removes the end-lines then a point,

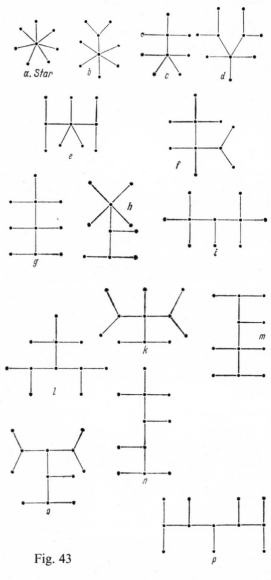

Fig. 43

the centre of the tree, is left.

If on the removal of end-lines one line is left, which naturally has

two-end points, then one has discovered a bi-centre, represented by
the two points and the line between them, known as the axis.

In general one does not come across centre or bi-centre after the
first removal of end-lines, so one repeats the removal of end-lines a
second time; if one still does not come across a centre or bi-centre,
then a third time, and so on. If after having removed the temporary
end-lines r times, one is left with a centre or bi-centre, then r is called
the radius of the tree. For example, the tree in Fig. 44 a has radius 2;

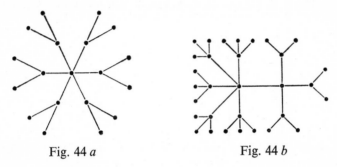

Fig. 44 a Fig. 44 b

it is not a star, but after the first removal of the end-lines one obtains
a star. Therefore, the tree has a centre. The tree in Fig. 44 b also has
radius 2, but has a bi-centre.

In a tree there is just one path from any one point to any other.
If one looks for the longest possible path from a point, then it will
certainly terminate at one of the end-points of the graph. The longest
path starting from an end-point is called the diameter.   In Fig. 44 a
the diameter $d = 4$, in Fig. 44 b, $d = 5$. Clearly, a diameter must pass
through the centre or bi-centre, and if d is even, the tree has a centre
while if d is odd the tree has a bi-centre.

Consider any one point of the tree and any line from it. Then we
call that tree, which is made up of this line and all points and lines
which join on the other end of this line, a branch.[1] The branch which
belongs to an end-point and its corresponding end-line is thus the
whole tree. To the centre of the tree of Fig. 44 a there belong six
branches; to the end-points of the axis of the tree represented in
Fig. 44 b belong four and six branches. The tree in Fig. 45 has an
axis with three branches at each of its two ends, that in Fig. 46 a
centre with three branches.

Let h_i be the number of lines belonging to the branch determined
by the line which leads from a point P to a neighbouring point Q_i.

[1] One should not think of the branch of a real tree!

Consider all neighbouring points Q_i; then the largest of the numbers h_i is called the height h of the point. We can then attach a number, the height, to each point of the tree. This has been done in Figs. 45 and 46; it is left to the reader in Figs. 44 a and 44 b.

Now in every tree there exists one point M or two points M_1 and M_2 with least height. If there is one point then it is called the mass-centre of the tree, if there are two points then these determine the mass-axis. Centre and mass-centre need not coincide, nor axis and mass-axis. In fact it can happen, as is shown by Figs. 45 and 46 on

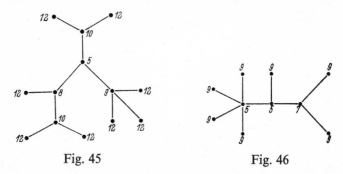

Fig. 45   Fig. 46

which the height of the individual points have been entered, that a tree with an axis has a mass-centre and a tree with a centre a mass-axis.

8. *Braids*

Starting with the structure of a braid as it is known in real life, we make the concept a little more precise in order that it should become accessible to a mathematical theory. An open braid is made up of single open threads whose mathematical representatives are space-curves. We restrict ourselves to a finite number of threads of finite length. The threads are stretched between the two parallel sides g_1 and g_2 of a rectangular frame, whose other two sides are h_1 and h_2. If there are n threads, then the sides g_1 and g_2 are divided into $n+1$ equal parts by a set of points $A_1, A_2, \ldots, A_n$ on g_1, $B_1, B_2, \ldots, B_n$ on g_2, the points being arranged in a fixed direction, say from left to right. The end points A_k and B_i of each of the n threads are known. At each point A, one and only one thread begins, and at each point B, one and only one thread terminates. In Fig. 47, where there are three threads, we have the correspondence

$$A_1 \longrightarrow B_2, \ A_2 \longrightarrow B_3, \ A_3 \longrightarrow B_1.$$

Imagine the thread-complex to be projected on to the plane of the rectangle, where the crossings show in the usual way which thread lies above and which below. No thread crosses the frame at top or bottom, or at the right or left. Thus the position of a thread as $A_1 \longrightarrow B_2$ or $A_3 \longrightarrow B_3$ in Fig. 48 is not permissible.

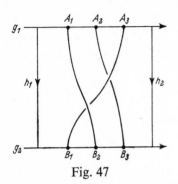

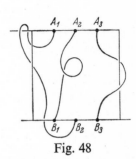

Fig. 47   Fig. 48

If it should happen that more than two threads cross at one point, then by a suitable change of position as previously explained, we can always arrange that a crossing involves two threads only.

Finally we impose the condition that any line parallel to the g-sides meets each thread once, and so all the n-threads exactly n-times. Thus for example, a loop as shown in the thread $A_2 \longrightarrow B_1$ in Fig. 48, is not allowed. Furthermore, the individual crossings are so distributed that a line parallel to the g-sides never cuts more than one crossing.

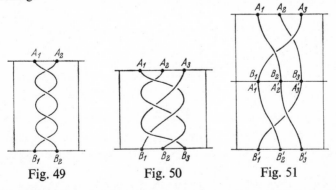

Fig. 49   Fig. 50   Fig. 51

As particular examples we show in Fig. 49 the two-braid and in Fig. 50 the usual three-braid. Naturally the simplest braid is the one given by $A_i \longrightarrow B_i$ in which no crossings occur.

Now if two braids Z and Z' have the same number of threads one can combine them (Fig. 51). If Z and Z' have frame edges g_1, g_2 and g'_1, g'_2, then one first puts $g_2 = g'_1$ (g_2 is covered by g'_1), and so $B_k = A'_k$ for all k. If one now allows $g_2 = g'_1$ to be suppressed then a new braid Z'' is formed, which is called the product of Z and Z'. This is expressed symbolically by

$$Z . Z' = Z''.$$

It is immediately clear that the combination of braids is associative, that is, for three braids Z_1, Z_2, Z_3 we have

$$(Z_1 . Z_2) . Z_3 = Z_1 . (Z_2 . Z_3).$$

In contrast, the commutative law does not hold in general, i.e. usually

$$Z_1 . Z_2 \neq Z_2 . Z_1.$$

We have imposed the condition that no two crossings can lie on a line parallel to the g-sides of the frame, therefore conversely, one can cut up a braid into a number of parts, so that in any one of the parts only one of the following three possibilities can occur:

1. There is no crossing among the n threads (Fig. 52 a). We denote such a braid by E, and since

$$Z . E = E . Z = Z$$

for all Z, we call E the unit band. Inserting or joining E to an existing braid does not alter its structure.

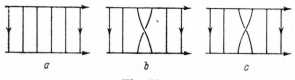

Fig. 52 a–c

2. The k-th thread, counted from the left along the top, crosses over the $(k + 1)$-th thread (Fig. 52 b). We call this operation s_k. In Fig. 52 b we have the operation s_2.

3. The k-th thread passes under the $(k + 1)$-th thread (Fig. 52 c). We call this operation s_k^{-1}, because the succession of the two operations s_k and s_k^{-1} cancel each other out if we join the two parts of the braid. In Fig. 52 c we have the operation s_2^{-1}.

We can now use the symbolic notation we have introduced to write down the expression for various examples of braids.[1] For the two-braid (Fig. 49) the expression is s_1^n, if the thread lying to the left crosses over the one to the right n-times (in Fig. 49 four times).

For the usual three-braid, the 'ladies' braid', the expression is $(s_1s_2^{-1})^n$, as can be read off from Fig. 50.

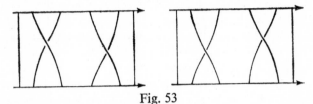

Fig. 53

For the upper part of the braid of Fig. 51 we have the expression $s_2^{-1}s_1$, for the lower part s_2s_1, thus for the whole braid $s_2^{-1}s_1s_2s_1$.

The reader should sketch for himself the common four-braid which has the expression $(s_1s_3s_2^{-1})^n$.

It is easily seen that the representation of a braid by these s-operations is not unique. The two braids in Fig. 53 are after all equivalent, but since the crossings in them change their relative heights above g_2, the expression s_1s_3 of the first is reversed in the second.

Just as to every s_k there is a corresponding s_k^{-1}, so that $s_ks_k^{-1} = E$, so to every Z there is also a Z^{-1}, so that $Z \cdot Z^{-1} = E$. One obtains Z^{-1} from Z by mirroring Z in g_2. This has been done in Fig. 54. The braid has been split up into its three parts, each with one crossing, and these then occur in

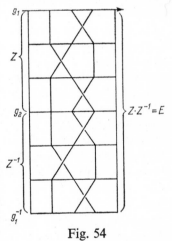

Fig. 54

the opposite order from g_2 to g_1^{-1}. One can inspect visually how the over- and under-crossings cancel each other out and how the whole forms a unit braid.

[1] E. ARTIN has developed a 'Theory of Braids', using the concept of a group.
Tr. The author has himself shown that braids with the same number of threads form a group, although he does not mention it explicitly in the text. He has defined the combination of two braids and the result is a similar braid. Associativity is mentioned and E is the unit braid. Finally at the end of § 8 the inverse of any braid is described.

9. *String, Rope, Cable*

In the previous paragraph we dealt with the combination of braids one after the other. With strings, ropes, cables and other such things, which in the mathematical sense all belong to the group of braids, we are faced with the juxtaposition of braids, or with braids within braids. Here the braids which are braided around each other are all of the same simple construction, namely, three, four or more elements twisted together. If there are three threads then the scheme is

Fig. 55

$(s_2s_1)^k$ and Fig. 55 shows the corresponding pattern of lines.

I give three examples of ropes. First a simple rope. An extraordinarily strong yarn is made by twisting hemp fibres, or some other material, in a right-handed sense. Then two or more lengths of yarn are twisted in a left-handed sense to make twine. A number of lengths of twine, the number depending on the thickness of the final rope, are twisted to the right into a strand. Finally three or four strands are twisted to the left. A rope constructed in this way is shortened (by the twisting) by 21% to 33% in comparison with the original fibres.

A very firm 'cabled' rope joins eight lengths of yarn into a strand (that is, it leaves out the formation of twine) four strands into a main strand, four main strands into a rope. A climber's rope, which is the speciality of the hemp works in Füssen (one of the biggest rope-makers in Germany), twists three yarns into twine, fifteen twine into a strand, three strands into rope. This rope has a green twine made of two yarns twisted together as a characteristic feature. It

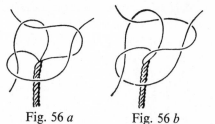

Fig. 56 *a*   Fig. 56 *b*

is twisted together with the other twine.

In all cases the direction in which the twisting takes place alters from step to step. Naturally the rope-makers have developed all sorts of machines for this work, part of which is done on the ropewalks.

Ropes exist which do not correspond to any of our three examples: one in common use is a cable with a core, the core being a straight thread about which the cords are twisted.

As far as I know, a particular theory of braids applied to these rope structures has not been developed. The theory would, for example, have to answer the question how to express the run of a single thread of yarn and would have to describe the composition of the rope and the twists where the twine runs in the direction of the rope.

Perhaps, instead of the rectangle in the theory of braids, one could take a circular cylinder, which would express the cyclic structure better.

If a sailor wishes to repair a snapped rope or make a decorative knot at the end of a rope he untwists three or four cords and laces their ends with each other. This he calls splicing.

Two twists are shown in Fig. 56 *a* and Fig. 56 *b*. One can be obtained from the other by interchanging over- and under-crossings. The sailor calls the first a crown knot, and the second a wall knot.

CHAPTER 5

A Single, Closed Thread

1. *Polygons*

A CONVEX n-gon is the simplest example of a closed line path which is topologically the same as a circle or an ellipse. The convex condition is not essential: the polygon could be dented, so long as the figure is without double-points, i.e. without intersections.

A chain of dominoes is also a valid example if the pieces at the beginning and end have the same number, and we arrange them so that these two touch. Another example is the path through a maze, where the entrance and exit coincide.

A closed line path lying in a plane divides it into an inside and an outside. If the polygon has e vertices and k lines then

$$e - k = 0.$$

If the figure does not lie in a plane, then it can be regularly projected on to the plane, so that the projected figure is without double points. The equation is also valid if the lines are replaced by topologically equivalent segments of curves, but not if, as for example with the circle, $e = 0$. Then one must (as we have already said in Chapter 2) put a point on the circumference of the circle.

A line path or curve (with a finite number of points) which goes to infinity in both directions does not meet the requirements of the equation: this difficulty may be overcome by regarding as one line the two line-segments which go to infinity. Alternatively the two line-segments may be regarded as having a common point at infinity.

2. *Intersections*

We have so far excluded intersections. In this paragraph, however, we shall examine (straight) line polygons and ask the question, How many double-point intersections are possible in an n-gon?

In a triangle no intersections are possible. In a quadrangle one intersection is possible. If we denote the number of intersections in a n-gon by I_n, then $I_3 = 0$, $I_4 = 0$ or 1.

An upper limit for I_n can be immediately determined. I_n cannot be greater than the number of pairs of non-neighbouring vertices, which implies

$$I_n \leqslant \frac{n(n-3)}{2}.$$

But can equality hold and are all cases 0, 1, 2, ... possible? The case $n = 4$ shows that both questions are to be answered in the negative. Fig. 57 shows the possible cases for $n = 5$. We see that

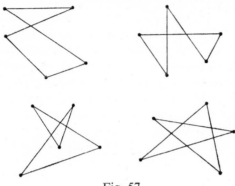

Fig. 57

here the maximum value of $I_5 = \frac{5 \cdot 2}{2} = 5$ is in fact achieved, but that in the series 0, 1, 2, ..., 5, the last-but-one value 4 is not attainable.

As the above cases suggest, one has in general to distinguish between odd and even n. The result, which we state here without proof,[1] is: if n is odd, then all cases in the series

$$0, 1, 2, \ldots, \frac{n(n-3)}{2}$$

with the exception of $\frac{n(n-3)}{2} - 1$ are possible. If n is even, then all cases

$$0, 1, 2, \ldots, \frac{n(n-4)}{2} + 1$$

are possible.

---

[1] E. STEINITZ remarks about the case n even: 'The statement that the number $\delta n \left[= \frac{n(n-4)}{2} + 1 \right]$ cannot be exceeded has not been proved, but it holds in every case verified.'

3. *Knights' Tours*

As is well known, the knight on the chessboard may always move
two squares parallel to the edges of the board and then one square

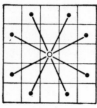

at right-angles to this motion. If he starts in the
middle of the chessboard as shown in Fig. 58,
he has eight possible moves. This number decreases if the starting point is nearer the edge
and decreases even more in a corner of the
board; just how much in each case the reader
will easily be able to decide.

Fig. 58

Consider the problem of passing through all
the 64 squares of the board in a connected
knight's tour. An example of such a path of 63 equally long lines
with 64 points is shown in Fig. 59 *a*; it is the knight's tour given
by DE MOIVRE.[1] With a few exceptions, the path beginning at the top
right completes a two-square wide frame, and then covers what is
left of the inner region of 4 × 4 squares.

One could further ask; are there also closed knights' tours? The
one just discussed is not closed. A closed knight's tour would be a

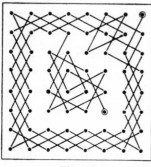

Fig. 59 *a*

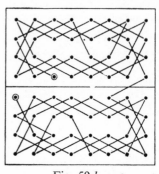

Fig. 59 *b*

64-gon, with intersections. An example of this is given in Fig. 59 *b*.
This knight's tour, which was given by EULER, has further properties.
If the board is divided in half by a line parallel to the top, then the
first half of the path is confined to half the board. The other half of
the path is then constructed centrally symmetric to the first half with
respect to the centre of the board. The starting point at the top left
in the lower half and the end point in the upper half are 'knighted'.
If one joins the two points by a line, then the knight's tour is a
closed 64-gon.

---

[1] ABRAHAM DE MOIVRE (1667–1754), private tutor, France, London.

Such a knight's tour can, of course, be begun at any point of the board; it represents, therefore, sixty-four different knights' tours, and it is clear that closed knights' tours exist from any square of the chessboard.

There are many questions connected with knights' tours and there is a rich literature on them, but we shall not go further into it here.

4. *Thread Games*

Thread-games are widespread over the whole world. Although at one time they were probably ancient rites, in the civilised countries they are now played only by children: elsewhere they are played by adults as well. A closed thread is held over both hands, and with the help of the fingers many varied spatial figures are constructed by all sorts of interlacing. Two different methods can be distinguished. In the first method, which is found, for example, in Australasia, a single person constructs the string figures. The sort of elaborate form which can arise is shown in Fig. 60. This figure is taken from a small collection of such games by J. KATTENTIDT: she calls the figure the great gate.

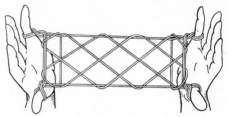

Fig. 60

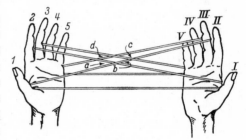

Fig. 61 *a*

In the thread-game played by children in Europe, two people take part. It is known as cat's cradle. One

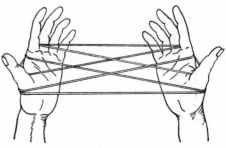

Fig. 61 *b*

person makes a string figure between his hands, and then another puts the fingers of both hands into the network of threads, and by taking the string off the first person obtains a new figure. Fig. 61 *a* and 61 *b* show an example. The first person, *A*, has constructed Fig. 61 *a*, the cradle, as it is called. I have numbered the fingers of both hands. One should imagine the fingers of the second person, *B*, to be numbered in the same way. *B* puts finger I into the angle *a*, II in angle *b*, 1 in *c* and 2 in *d*. Both fingers of each hand hold the cross taut and pull it outwards, i.e. away from the mid-point of the figure, so far that the fingers come outside the horizontal threads of the cradle. Then he pulls the cross down and in a circle round the horizontal threads, until the fingers of both hands touch below the figure. Then *B* turns his hands so far that the fingers point upwards and pushes his hands upwards. As he does this *A* pulls his hands out of the figure. *B* now lets go of the cross, which he had so far held taut, and spreads his thumb and forefinger. Fig. 61 *b* is then obtained.

The above description is long, difficult and probably unintelligible if one does not already know the game; nevertheless children learn the process quickly and surely, picking it up from each other. Sometimes it is easier to make something with one's hands than to describe it in words.

As in § 3 with all closed knights' tours, so here all the many different figures constructed in thread-games are topologically equivalent to the circle.

5. *Knots*

A privileged topic of topological research is the theory of knots.[1] By the term knot one understands any closed line or thread twisted in space. It must be emphasised once again that in the mathematical sense knots are closed threads, diverging from common linguistic usage where one speaks of knots even if the thread is not closed. One speaks, for example, of making a knot in one's handkerchief if one has forgotten something, and of knotting a tie round one's neck, but these are not knots to the mathematician.

A question: in front of me on the desk sits a fly. It annoys me and

[1] From the rich literature I mention only K. REIDEMEISTER, *Knotentheorie* (*Ergebnisse der Mathematik* I, 1, 1932) (Springer, Berlin), and a fine introduction taken from a lecture of H. TIETZE, *Ein Kapitel Topologie* (*Hamburger Mathematische Einzelschriften*, 36th Tract, 1932) (Teubner, Leipzig). Both works give full references to further literature on knot theory and allied topics.

I drive it away. It buzzes round the room but then lands again in the same place as before. Could it describe a knot in its flight or not?

But back to the theory! Let us again work in terms of a spatial figure represented normed and regular, in the sense of Chapter 2,

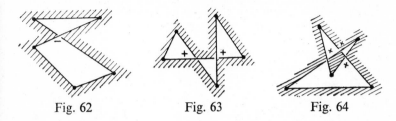

Fig. 62   Fig. 63   Fig. 64

in the plane. Using this we will describe another method of distinguishing knots, giving simple examples. Our first examples will be the pentagons with one, two, three or five crossings regarded as knots, (Figs. 62 to 65), the two trefoil knots (Fig. 67) and the two figures-of-eight (Fig. 68).

First we will introduce a notation for the type of crossings. Since the representation is regular we have only two line-segments at each crossing, one line being regarded as lying above and the other below. Imagine now that the whole region outside the representation of the knot is shaded.

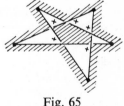

Fig. 65

Of the simple closed interior regions, those which touch the outer region at crossings only are shaded. That such inner regions do not always occur is shown by the pentagons with one and two crossings (Figs. 62 and 63). If necessary we shade

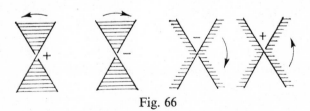

Fig. 66

any further region which is connected to an already shaded region at crossings only. Then the whole knot-diagram is separated into shaded and unshaded regions. Along any line-segments a shaded and unshaded region are always contiguous. At every crossing two shaded and two unshaded regions meet, and they are always diagonally opposite each other.

Consider a single crossing. The upper line-segment can be rotated about the crossing point into the direction of the lower line-segment in such a way that the former passes over the shaded regions. Then there are two possibilities: either the rotation is left-handed, that is a mathematically positive rotation, or it is right-handed, that is,

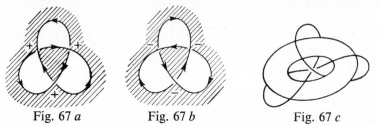

Fig. 67 *a*   Fig. 67 *b*   Fig. 67 *c*

a mathematically negative rotation (the hand of a clock describes a mathematically negative rotation). For a positive rotation we attach a + to the crossing and for a negative one a —. Fig. 66 shows four crossings, and in all our examples Figs. 62 to 68 the + and — signs and the shaded regions have been entered, with the exception of Fig. 67 *c*.

We call a knot alternately normed if when we follow the thread round continuously we pass through the crossings alternately above and below. Naturally not all knots are alternate, but if one has a

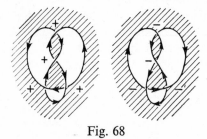

Fig. 68

regular but not yet normed diagram in the plane, then one can always norm the diagram in such a way that the corresponding knot is alternate. If a knot diagram has been normed alternately, then a second alternate norming can be obtained by re-arrangement, i.e. by inter-changing over-crossings and under-crossings.[1]

Consider an unshaded region of any alternately normed knot diagram; if we move round the region and in so doing pass along a line-segment from an under-crossing to a neighbouring over-crossing, then there is always another path along a line-segment from an under-crossing to an over-crossing. This continues until we have gone round the whole unshaded region. The sense in which such a path

[1] *Tr.* This can be done by turning the knot over.

round the unshaded region has been described is either always positive or always negative according to the norming.

But if we describe such a path round a shaded region, then the sense of the path is opposite to that of the unshaded regions of the same knot diagram. This is also true for the shaded outer region of the diagram, where for any circuit in the given sense the region lies to the right if for any interior shaded region it lay to the right, and to the left if it lay to the left.

We mention explicitly that in this circuit of the various inner regions the direction in which the thread-segments are traversed changes constantly.

It is clear that for a non-alternate normed knot it is not possible to determine a circuit in this way. For if two neighbouring crossings are not alternate, then it is not possible to describe a line-segment from an under-crossing to an over-crossing and so the criterion is lost.

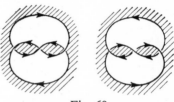

Fig. 69

We mention two further knots. If in the interior of an alternately normed shaded knot there is one and only one shaded region then the knot is called a torus knot.[1] Our examples in Figs. 64, 65 and 67 are torus knots. If there are two such shaded regions, then it is called a pretzel knot,[2] or simply a pretzel. The two figures-of-eight of Fig. 68 are such knots, as are the two-braid knots (Fig. 69).

6. *The Isotopy Problem*

We have discussed in the previous paragraph various notations and characterisations of knots and their representations in the plane. Knots which can be transformed into each other by continuous deformations are called isotopic. We shall call all knots which are isotopic to one another a class of knots (one sometimes uses the single word 'knot' to mean 'class of knots'). We single out one class of knots in particular, that of all knots which are isotopic to the circle.

Consider the problem of deciding whether two given knots are

---

[1] The name is derived from the fact that the knot can be wrapped round a torus, as Fig. 67 c shows for the trefoil knot.
[2] One can wrap a pretzel knot round a pretzel.

E

isotopic, that is whether they belong to the same class. If one makes a string model, for example, of a two-braid knot (Fig. 69), it is simple to turn this into a trefoil; one two-braid knot becomes one trefoil and the other the other trefoil. As the two trefoil knots are symmetric to each other, so are the two two-braid knots. One trefoil knot is thus shown to be isotopic to the one two-braid knot, and the other to the other one.

One can always change one knot into another of its class using its plane representation instead of the spatial model. One has to describe those operations which are obvious visually from the spatial model. We have already met the operations O_1 and O_2 in § 2 of Chapter 3 and we add another operation O_3 which is clear from Fig. 70. The thread 3, which crosses over the crossed threads 1 and 2, alters its position. The reader should change a two-braid knot to a trefoil, restricting himself to the operations O_1, O_2 and O_3.

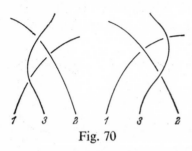

Fig. 70

Fig. 68 represents two figures-of-eight symmetric to each other. Here also experiment will show that it is possible to transform one into the other. The reader can try this for himself. But the two trefoil knots show that knots symmetric to each other are not by any means always isotopic: LISTING,[1] one of the first mathematicians to be interested in knots (on the whole experimentally), used the word amphicheiral to describe symmetric isotopic knots. Figures-of-eight are thus amphicheiral, while trefoils and therefore also the two-braid knots, are not.

Consider the knot which one makes in the tie round one's throat. (Naturally the ends must be considered as joined so that it is a knot in our sense.) If one loosens the tie and pulls it off over one's head, then one finds either a simple knot which is isotopic to the circle or a firmer knot which is isotopic to one of the two trefoil knots, depending on whether the maker of the knot is right- or left-handed.

We remind the reader at this point of a well-known party game. The person who is to play is told to take an open string, holding the two ends in his two hands, and to tie a knot in the topological circle formed by the string, arms and upper part of his body. In spite of the most unbelievable contortions he fails. There is a simple solution:

[1] J. B. LISTING (1808–1882) was professor at the University of Göttingen.

before picking up the string one should cross one's hands in front of one's chest. By the way, which knot does one obtain?

Now the mathematician investigating isotopy cannot be satisfied with experimental procedures such as we have described. If it were only a matter of a finite number of possible transformations one could still be satisfied with experiment, even if it were obvious that the number would be very large. But, in fact, the number is infinite. I could, for instance, attach to the three curves (meshes in our previous terminology) of the trefoil knot arbitrarily long two-braids by continually forming loops.

This structure would of course be recognised at a glance; nevertheless it shows the possibility of complicating a knot arbitrarily. Further, one could crumple the braids into a ball and twist them about and so obtain ever new knots all of which were isotopic to the trefoil knot.

In the development, up to the present time, of mathematical methods to determine the isotopy class of knots, two approaches have been principally used. The first approach uses number theory, and in particular the theory of quadratic forms. In this method one makes use of the shaded regions and signed crossings of a regular, normed representation of the knot, and associates a certain quadratic form with each knot. The second method uses group theory. Thus one can, for example, using number theory methods, prove that the symmetric trefoil knots are not isotopic. This was first proved rigorously by DEHN. If one regards the star pentagon as an alternate knot then there are two knots symmetric to each other, depending on the way in which the pentagon is normed. These two Simony knots,[1] as they are called, are not isotopic, as can be proved by group theory methods. A complete set of criteria for isotopy still awaits discovery. Given two string models or two projected figures of knots, no general criterion is known to date which one could apply to decide whether or not the two knots are isotopic. Since we have restricted our discussion to visual topology, it is not the place here to investigate further the two analytic methods we have mentioned which give a partial solution to the problem.

If the general goal is too far away, one can state a nearer one. Just as the botanist lists the types of plants and the zoologist the animals, so one can list the knots according to some principle and put them on record. In the tract by TIETZE two tables are given from such

---

[1] Named after OSCAR SIMONY (1852–1915) who did mainly experimental work on the knot problem.

classifications, which naturally deal only with knots of less than a stated degree of complexity. The first table of knots with ten crossings is by TAIT, the other of non-alternate knots, is by C. N. LITTLE.[1] REIDEMEISTER at the end of his book gives a table of knots following ALEXANDER and BRIGGS, with three, four, etc. up to nine crossings. The trefoil has three crossings, the figure-of-eight four; of the two knots with five crossings we know the one of SIMONY. In Fig. 71 the other five-knot and the three six-knots are drawn. They are un-normed since two alternate forms which are symmetric to each other occur. The most obvious knot with seven crossings is the seven-star.

Fig. 71

There are six others. Twenty-one eight-knots and 49 nine-knots have been shown to exist. The regular, normed projection of any knot can be operated on by O_1, O_2 and O_3 and be brought into a form with a minimum number of crossings. This minimum number is clearly an invariant, but there is no general method for its determination in any given case. The same is also true for another knot invariant, the minimum number of regions which occur in a regular projection.

7. Wreaths

We refer back to the braids which we treated in § 8 of Chapter 4. We imagine the plane of the rectangular frame bent round into a cylinder, so that g_1 and g_2, and thereby the points A_i and B_i, coincide. Thus a closed braid (wreath) is made. We consider the axis of the cylinder as an impassable barrier, but otherwise the threads are allowed to leave the surface of the cylinder.

Now there are two possibilities; either there are many or there is only a single closed thread. The simplest case of the first possibility is that of the unit braid, that is the case of k closed threads which, topologically, may be regarded as circles. With a closed two-braid we obtain an interlinking of two closed circles (Fig. 72) if the number of crossings is even, or one single but knotted thread (Fig. 73)

[1] I quote beside TIETZE the two papers: TAIT, *On Knots*, Part III, C. N. LITTLE *Non-alternate knots* (*Transactions of the Royal Society of Edinburgh*, 32 (1887) and 39 (1900)).

if the number of crossings is odd. We will leave the case of such interlinkings until we come back to it in the next chapter, and restrict ourselves to the case of a single, knotted thread. Fig. 74 gives a further example: a three-fold knot.

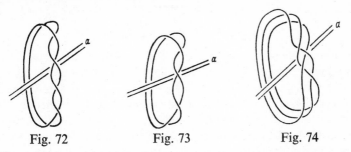

Fig. 72   Fig. 73   Fig. 74

One notices that such wreaths consisting of single threads are nothing but knots. Using the characteristic expressions introduced for braids, the braid with two threads $Z = s_1^3$ (as well as the braid $Z' = s_1^{-3}$, which is symmetric to it) leads to the trefoil knot. The 'lady's braid' $Z = (s_1 s_2^{-1})^2$ with three threads leads to the double loop.

Conversely, one can change a knot into a closed braid, although not uniquely.

CHAPTER 6

Line-systems with Closed Paths

1. *Euler's Theorem for a Polygonal Net*

IN CHAPTER 4, § 4 we called a line-complex closed if it had no end-points and no end-lines. We will refer to this as a polygonal net. Let the number of points again be e, the number of line-segments (edges) be k, and the number of polygons with non-intersecting sides of which the net is composed, be f. This last number is also the number of simple closed paths in the line-system each of which enclose exactly one polygon (paths enclosing polygons composed of two or more separate polygons are not included).

We examine the expression

$$I_2 = e - k + f.$$

If in any one of the polygons which compose the net one draws a diagonal, then k and f are each increased by 1, thus I_2 remains unchanged. If one continues this process, one can transform the polygonal net into a triangular net without changing the value of I_2.

A bounding triangle may be attached to the net by only one point, or by two points and thus with one edge, or by three points and thus with two edges. If one removes such a bounding triangle, then besides the triangular surface, two points and three edges are removed in the first case, one point and two edges in the second, and no points and one edge in the third. In all three cases I_2 remains unaltered.

One can in this way successively reduce the polygonal net from its boundary, without changing I_2. Since in the end only one triangle with $I_2 = 1$ remains, I_2 must have been 1 from the very beginning. Thus for a polygonal net or closed line-complex

$$e - k + f = 1.$$

The simplest special case is a (closed) polygon without double-points.

If at any vertices of the closed line-system end-lines are added, then the invariant I_2 does not alter, since in the case of each end-line one more line and one more point are added; e and k are always increased by 1, and their difference remains unchanged.

Instead of reducing the polygonal net from the boundary one can reduce it from the inside obtaining finally a polygon with $I_2 = 1$.

2. *Hamilton's Dodecahedron Game*[1]

The Irish mathematician HAMILTON[2] published a mathematical pastime which uses a board connected with the polygonal net obtained from a dodecahedron. Among the five regular solids there is, as is well known, one which is bounded by twelve regular pentagons. Since topologically it is immaterial that the surfaces are all congruent we will project it from some point on to a plane: we choose the centre of projection near the middle of one of the side-faces, so that we get the picture of Fig. 75. A regular pentagon surrounds the whole closed line-complex, in the middle appears a regular pentagon rotated through 36° (which is the projection of the opposite face) and between the two there is a decagon which forms the boundary between the set of five pentagons bordering on the inner pentagon, and the five pentagons bordering the outer contour.

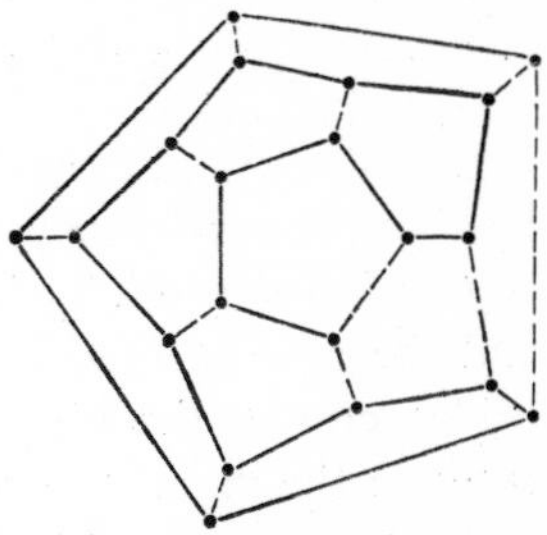

Fig. 75

Now the problem is to pass through all the twenty vertices, in one connected path; no line may be traversed twice during the circuit. Since the number of edges is thirty, eleven remain unused. Fig. 75 itself gives a solution, the untrodden edges being dashed. The reader should consider whether one can choose the starting point arbitrarily and if, having chosen the starting point, there exists more than one solution. He should look for a path which under the same conditions leads back to the origin.

AHRENS has given this Hamiltonian tour an interesting form. He poses the problem of making a tour through twenty German university towns, so that each town is visited exactly once and that the traveller, who must choose two roads from the three roads at his disposal from each town, returns to his starting point. I will give such an itinerary and ask the reader to draw a geographically corresponding dodecahedron: Berlin—Breslau—Königsberg—Kiel—Bonn—München—Erlangen—Tübingen—Freiburg—Strassburg—Marburg—Göttingen—Rostock—Greifswald—Halle—Giessen—Heidelberg—Wurzburg—Jena—Leipzig—Berlin.

Suppose now that in this series Breslau, Königsberg and Strassburg

---

[1] *Tr.* See CLAUDE BERGE, *The Theory of Graphs*, pp. 107 ff.
[2] W. R. HAMILTON, 1805–1865, published the game in 1856.

are removed. The reader should substitute Hamburg, Münster Frankfurt a.M. and put the itinerary into a suitable order.

The tetrahedron and the cube lead to similar tour problems. Corresponding dually to the dodecahedron is the icosahedron and to the cube the octahedron. The nets of these solids give rise to the duals of the exercise just described, namely to find tours in which precisely all the twenty (or eight) surfaces are transversed. These also are left to the reader for his own investigation.

3. *The Königsberg Bridges Problem*

Fig. 76 *a* shows the centre of Königsberg. An island (the Kneiphof) has been formed between the old and the new Pregel by cutting a connecting channel. Today the old Pregel is crossed by two bridges, and the new by one. Five bridges lead to the Kneiphof, and one bridge crosses the Pregel; this bridge also acts as a railway link between the main station and the north station. This last bridge is new, as is the second bridge over the old Pregel.

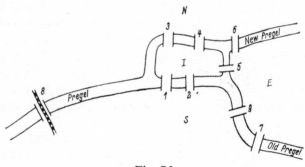

Fig. 76 *a*

In the 18th century the question was asked: Is a walk possible, in which all the bridges (there were then seven) are crossed exactly once? We immediately ask, further, what is the answer to this question when the railway bridge is added as an eighth, and what now that the ninth bridge crosses the old Pregel?

One can, of course, experiment—and that more easily on paper than on the paving stones of Königsberg. There is only a finite number of possibilities but this number, as one can quickly convince oneself, is quite large. Therefore, a general solution is more profitable, the more so since one can apply it to all problems of a similar nature.[1] Take, for example, the present state of affairs with nine bridges. The river-system divides the town into four regions, the island I, the northern part of the town N, the southern part S and the eastern part E. We represent these parts of the town by the points I, N, S and E. Edges 1 and 2 lead across the bridges from I to S, edges 3 and 4 from I to N and edge 5 to E. Beside these there is line 6 from E to N, 7 and 9 to S, and finally edge 8 from N to S. Fig. 76 b shows this road network as a line-complex.

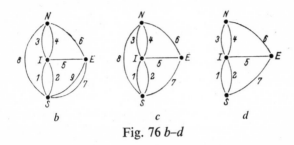

Fig. 76 b–d

If one wants to use each edge once only in a connected walk, then it is essential that to each edge which one uses to reach a point there must correspond another edge on which one can continue the walk. That means that the number of edges that meet at any point must be even. There may only be two exceptions; the point at which one begins the journey and that at which one finishes. At these points an odd number of edges may meet.

Consider the line-system Fig. 76 b. At N and E the number of edges is even, at I and S it is odd. Therefore, if a walk of the required type is possible at all, it must begin at I and end at S, or the reverse.

When bridge 9 did not exist then the line-system was that of Fig. 76 c. At N and S there are an even number of edges, at I and E an odd number. In this case, if a walk is at all possible it must begin at E and end at I, or the reverse.

Finally consider the state of affairs at the time of Euler, that is without bridges 8 and 9 (Fig. 76 d). At that time an odd number of edges met at all four points; the desired walk was thus impossible.

---

[1] It is ascribed to L. EULER (1707–1783). He was born in Basel and became a member of the Petersburg, then the Berlin and then again the Petersburg academy.

4. *Unicursal Curves*

The bridge problem treated in § 3 suggests the general question of a criterion for the existence of a walk along a closed connected line-system in which each edge is used exactly once. There are popular amusements in which one has to decide whether any given, more or less complicated, figure is a unicursal system. The hexagon formed by two equilateral triangles on top of each other is a unicursal figure, a rectangle with its two diagonals, however, is not. The string with which one ties up a parcel is usually unicursal for the sake of economy.

We have already discovered a necessary condition for a connected line-system to be unicursal. The number of edges at each point must be even (then the starting point and the end point of the walk are coincident) or there may be two exceptional points with an odd number of edges (then these two are the starting and end points of the walk). We will now show that this condition is also sufficient.

We begin by considering the first case in which the number of edges at each point is even. We choose any walk leaving and returning to a point P and delete every edge used. If no edge remains the case is finished. Suppose that something remains. Since at each point through which we have passed an even number of edges have been removed (two if the point has been crossed once, four if it has been crossed twice, etc.), the remainder is a system in which all points have an even number of edges. We shall refer to such points as even points. There are now two possibilities: either one closed line-system is left or there are many. In the first case we again set out from P, finish at P and again have two possibilities. If one line-system remains each time then the case can be completed in this way. What happens, however, if at any time the system breaks up into two or more line-systems? Assume that some line-system L has broken off. This could only have happened if, when we came to some point Q of the severed system, we immediately returned to our main system. Now from Q take a walk in L which ends at Q. This is certainly possible since L has only even points. Assume that all the edges in Q are thus used up. Then when Q is reached in the original walk, one has only to insert this new walk which begins and ends at Q. Make such an insertion for each severed line-system and also if in one of the severed systems fresh separations occur. However complicated the system may be, since we have a line-system with a finite number of points and edges, one can always obtain a closed path, which uses all edges of the system once only, by making a finite number of such insertions.

The case with two odd points, which have to be chosen as beginning and end points, can be settled in the following way. Begin with a walk which connects these two points and then, as in the previous case, make all necessary insertions.

Thus our necessary criterion for unicursal line-systems has been shown to be also sufficient.

5. *Dominoes*

The game known by this name consists of a number of 'pieces' which have a rectangular shape, such that one pair of sides is twice as long as the other. Each of the two squares which make up the rectangle has a number on it. These numbers are neither Arabic nor Roman numerals, but of the form usually found on dice or cards, like the numeral pictures which are sometimes used in the first lessons in arithmetic.

Depending on the size of the game, all combinations of the numbers $0, 1, 2, \ldots n$ taken two at a time (with repetitions) are represented by pieces; one of the two numbers is put in each square. Therefore, if for example $n = 4$, there are the following pieces:

0,0; 0,1; 0,2; 0,3; 0,4; 1,1; 1,2; 1,3; 1,4; 2,2; 2,3; 2,4; 3,3; 3,4; 4,4.

For $n = 6$ we have the seven double numbers and also, since combining each of the seven numbers with the six others would give each number pair exactly twice, we have a further $\frac{7 \cdot 6}{2} = 21$ pieces.

The total is, therefore, 28 pieces.

We now investigate the possibility of arranging all the dominoes in a connected series so that one number on one piece always touches the same number on its neighbour.

Let us first examine the solution of the problem for the case $n = 4$. We can leave aside the five pieces with double numbers. We can always insert them afterwards into the chain of other pieces, for example, we can insert the piece 1,1, in the chain where 1 and 1 touch, or, if 1 occurs at the beginning or end of the chain, we can add it there.

Draw a pentagon with all its diagonals, and label the vertices 0, 1, 2, 3 and 4. The intersections of the diagonals are not counted as points of this line-complex, each of whose lines represent one of the ten dominoes with different numbers. One will be able to arrange all the dominoes in a connected chain if one can pass along the figure unicursally. Since four lines, i.e. an even number, meet in each point, this is possible and the problem has a solution. We can, for example, read off from Fig. 77 the following solution in which the double numbers can be inserted afterwards in suitable places:

$$0,1; \ 1,2; \ 2,3; \ 3,4; \ 4,2; \ 2,0; \ 0,3; \ 3,1; \ 1,4; \ 4,0.$$

The case $n = 6$ corresponds to the unicursal walk along a septagon with all its diagonals. In this case six lines always meet at each of the seven vertices, i.e. an even number. The figure is thus unicursal, and each uni-cursal path, with the insertion of the double numbers, gives one of the de-sired chains of all the dominoes.

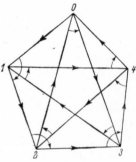

Fig. 77

For each even n it is possible to draw the corresponding unicursal curve. The path is closed since an even number of lines run from each vertex. This means that in the chain of dominoes the first and last numbers are the same.

Now consider n odd. In the case $n = 1$, only the open chain $0,0; 0,1; 1,1$ is possible. For $n > 1$, however, there is no chain whatsoever. For $n = 3$ one has a quadrilateral with its diagonals as the corresponding figure, and this is not unicursal. A corresponding state of affairs exists in all other cases where n is odd.

One can ask, How many possible solutions, open and closed, are there? This is answered, for example, by AHRENS for $n = 4$ and $n = 6$; in the first case there are 63,360 and in the second $3,979,614,965,760 = 2^{12}.3^8.5.7.4231$ open chains. Since this question is of little interest in our topological investigations, the calculation is left to the reader as also is the investigation of the general case for even n.

6. Ferrying

A well-known story told long ago by ALCUIN,[1] describes how a man ferries across a river three things, which are, to some extent, mutually inimical: a wolf, a goat and a cabbage. He cannot leave the wolf and goat alone, nor the goat and cabbage, but the wolf naturally will not

[1] ALCUIN (735–804), an Anglo-Saxon at the court of Charles the Great.

touch the cabbage. The boat is so small, that he can only take with him one of the three on any one trip. How does he do it?

A solution can quite easily be found by trial, but we shall use a systematic method of line-complexes. Before doing this we will consider a very simple ferry problem in order to elucidate the method to be adopted.

An adult stands on one bank of a stream; on the other side are two children and a small boat, which can hold two children or one grown-up, but not one child and one adult together. The problem is: how does the adult get to the two children? First we list the possible ways in which three persons can be arranged on the banks of the stream. To the left of each vertical bar the people on the left bank are shown, to the right those on the right. A denotes an adult, C a child and the possibilities are numbered. We have, therefore, the following six possibilities

$$A \mid CC \ldots 1, \qquad CC \mid A \ldots 2,$$
$$AC \mid C \ldots 3, \qquad C \mid AC \ldots 4,$$
$$- \mid ACC \ldots 5, \qquad ACC \mid - \ldots 6,$$

where a dash denotes that no one is on that particular bank. Position 6 is useless; the initial position is 1 and the final position is 5.

We now construct a line-complex, whose five points correspond to the five positions we have just given. Every line corresponds to one crossing. We will arrange the points as the vertices of a regular pentagon (Fig. 78 a). From position 1 it is only possible to go to position 3, since the boat

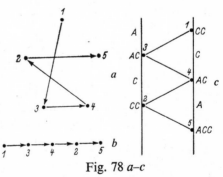

Fig. 78 a–c

is with the children and is not at the disposal of the adult (and position 6 is not considered). From 3 one goes to 4 since, although possible, the passage to 1 only results in the previous state of affairs. From 4, 3 being retrogressive, the next crossing leads to position 2 and from there to the desired final position 5. Thus the line-complex of Fig. 78 a is formed. We can represent it in the form of Fig. 78 b, or in the form of Fig. 78 c if we want to picture the crossings over the river.

Now to the problem of ALCUIN. Let F denote the ferry-man with his boat, W the wolf, G the goat and C the cabbage. We begin by setting up a table of the possible positions and we number them. If we denote the left and the right bank of the river by the left- and right-hand side of a vertical bar, we have

$$FWGC \mid - \ldots 1, \qquad \qquad - \mid FWGC \ldots 6,$$
$$FWC \mid G \ldots 2, \qquad \qquad G \mid FWC \ldots 7,$$
$$FWG \mid C \ldots 3, \qquad \qquad C \mid FWG \ldots 8,$$
$$FGC \mid W \ldots 4, \qquad \qquad W \mid FGC \ldots 9,$$
$$FG \mid WC \ldots 5, \qquad \qquad WC \mid FG \ldots 10.$$

One must, of course, decide which of all the possible positions are consistent with the conditions; $F \mid WGC$ or $WG \mid FC$ are not permissible. On the other hand all permissible positions must be listed.

We again arrange the ten points which represent the different positions on a circle, and examine which of the paths leading from point 1 to point 6 are consistent with our conditions.

Since the ferry-man is necessary for the crossing, the edges from 1 to 2, 3, 4, 5 are impossible; since three cannot get into the boat, the edges to 6, 7, 8, 9 are also impossible. The only remaining edge is from 1 to 10. The next crossing leads to 2, there being no other possibility; the goat cannot row the boat, and one does not want to go back to the initial position 1. But now there are two possibilities;

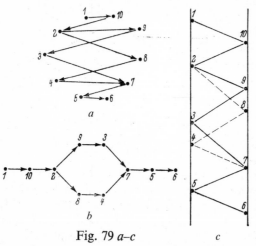

a

b

Fig. 79 a–c

c

one can either leave the cabbage or the wolf behind and ferry the other across. Thus one can go from 2 either to 9 or to 8.

To begin with let us follow through the first case. How can one continue from 9? Either the cabbage or the goat must be taken. But if the ferry-man takes the cabbage with him he goes back to the previous position 2. So he takes the goat with him and gets to position 3. From here the next crossing leads to position 7. He takes the wolf along, since with the goat he would again return to the previous position. Wolf and goat may now not remain together, so the ferry-man, in order to create a new situation, takes along the goat and comes to position 5. From 5 the last crossing leads to the goal 6.

Now to the second possibility leading, instead, from position 2 to position 8. From 8 one goes to 4, the wolf remaining behind alone. From 4 one goes to 7, the ferry-man rows the cabbage over, and now the subsequent sequence is along the same path as in the first case.

We can now change the circular scheme of the line-complex (Fig. 79 *a*) into the clearer Fig. 79 *b*, which we can also put in the form of Fig. 79 *c* if we wish to demonstrate the crossings of the stream. In this example we do not have a tree, but the line-complex forms a cycle.

7. *Decanting*

Probably the oldest example of a decanting problem is the following. Given three vessels, the first holding 8 litres, the second 5 and the third 3, one is required to divide into equal quantities the liquid contained in the largest vessel. Expressed arithmetically, one must transform the state (8, 0, 0) to the state (4, 4, 0) by a series of states (x, y, z), where

$$x + y + z = 8,$$
$$0 \leqslant x \leqslant 8, \quad 0 \leqslant y \leqslant 5, \quad 0 \leqslant z \leqslant 3$$

and x, y, z are respectively the contents of the first, second and third vessel. Also since at least one of the vessels must always be empty or full, at least one of the equations

$$x = 0, \quad x = 8, \quad y = 0, \quad y = 5, \quad z = 0, \quad z = 3$$

must always be valid. Under these conditions, there are in all the following 16 possible states (I omit brackets and commas):

800, 710, 701, 620, 602, 530, 503, 440, 413, 350, 323, 251, 233, 152, 143, 053.

We regard the 16 states as points of a line-complex and distribute the points at equal intervals on the circumference of a circle (Fig. 80).

One must begin by considering which lines are permissible as representing the change from one state to another under the given conditions. One cannot, for example, go from 800 to 440, but one can go to 503 or 350. Therefore 800 can be joined to 503 and to 350. Some of these lines are passable in both directions, for example the two just named. But whereas one can go from 710 to 800, for example, the opposite direction is impossible. I leave it to the reader to list the possible changes of state and to enter them into the 16-gon.

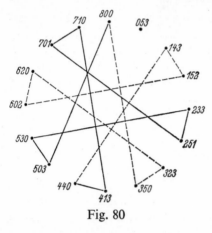

Fig. 80

A solution of the exercise is now to find a connected path from 800 to 440, in which only allowed lines— taking into account direction —are used. Two such paths are entered in Fig. 80, the one shown by continuous lines, the other by dashed lines. The length of the path is not the same in both cases; in the one case eight, and in the other case seven, lines are needed. The latter is the shortest path, i.e. the distance of the point 440 from 800.

The two paths together pass through all the points except for the point 053 which remains isolated. But if the shortness of the path is immaterial, one can easily include the point 053. One can reach it directly from 503, and from 053 one can go to 350, say, and thus join up with the previous net of lines. This result shows, therefore, that for any arbitrarily chosen state, there is a possible decanting to any other state.

8. *Loss of Ancestors in a Genealogical Tree*

Some time ago there appeared in a Munich carnival newspaper a note to the following effect. It is a mistake to assume that in earlier times there were less people on the earth. Everyone has two parents, four grandparents, etc. If one goes back ten generations, then one has already $2^{10} = 1024$ ancestors. Hence, 300 years ago ($300 = 10 \times 30$) there were about one thousand times as many people on the earth. Again, twenty generations ago, that is approximately 600 years, there were $2^{20} \approx 1$ million times as many, and so on. This fallacy, which has been widely disseminated, can be solved by noting that the farther one goes back the more 'ancestor loss' occurs. After all, all people are more or less related to each other.

The 'normal' family tree is a tree in the mathematical sense, characterised by the strict adherence to a dichotomy. Every person has a father and a mother. But as soon as ancestor loss occurs the family tree loses its tree character; we have then a line-complex with closed paths. Fig. 81 shows the graph of a family tree in which cousins married; instead of eight great-grandparents there are only six.

AHRENS refers to a family tree in which there are two ancestors in the first generation, four in the second, but in the third instead of eight persons there are only four,

Fig. 81

although cousins do not marry. For this example I have drawn in Fig. 82 the corresponding line-complex. This is the family tree of DON CARLOS. The key to the numbered points on the graph reads as follows: 1. Don Carlos (1545–1568), 2. Philip II (1527–1598), 3. Maria of Portugal (1527–1545), 4. Charles V (1500–1558), 5. Isabella of Portugal (1503–1539), 6. John II (King of Portugal) (1502–1557), 7. Catherine of Austria (1507–1578), 8. Philip I of Spain (1478–1506), 9. Emanuel I (King of Portugal) (1469–1521), 10. Maria of Spain, 11. Joanna the Mad (1479–1555).

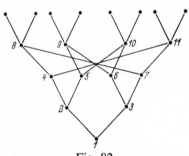

Fig. 82

The next generation is in perfect dichotomous continuation and numbers eight ancestors.

The remarkable family trees which often result when one takes account of step-parents and step-brothers and how a person may be strangely related to himself, will not be investigated here. The reader may himself put them into line-complex form, if, as happens not infrequently, such cases appear in magazines, etc.

9. *Mazes Again*

We will demonstrate the connection between mazes and line-complexes in a further example. I have chosen one of the drawings which

F

the psychologists use for intelligence tests (Fig. 83). The candidate is asked to draw with a pencil a connected path from the entrance to the shaded centre. This is, of course, very easy in the given case.

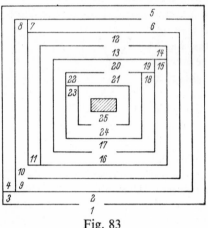

Fig. 83

As points of the line-complex corresponding to the maze we choose on the one hand the ends of all culs-de-sac, and on the other the positions in front of and behind every entry from one passage to another. The lines joining points will then be those paths which are permitted in the maze. The crossing of an entry is also counted as a path.

In Fig. 84 we have arranged the twenty-five points in an arbitrary order (instead of the rectangular pattern we could, for example, have used a sequence of points in a circle) and we have entered the walkable connections between these points. Fig. 85 shows a somewhat simpler graph representing the same situation; it is a tree except for the circle at its end point. Of course, there are mazes which correspond to simple or multiple closed graphs. The reader can invent such mazes for himself, or try drawing the graph corresponding to the quite complicated maze at Hampton Court (Fig. 21).

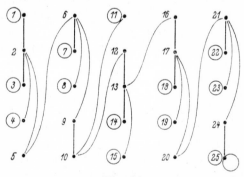

Fig. 84

The instruction for traversing a maze, given in Chapter 3, § 6, has, as we pointed out, the drawback that all passages may not be used. We showed in the Hampton Court example that 'islands' remained. CHR. WIENER, who mentions this solution, gives another solution

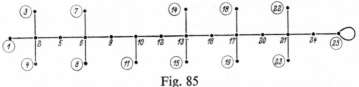

Fig. 85

which overcomes this deficiency. We describe this general solution in terms of the corresponding graph. (In practice it is better if instead of sidling along the wall one walks down the middle of the passage; thus it is presumed that one ignores the width of the passage.)

From the starting point A, choose any line AB and continue until either an end-point Q of the graph, or a point Q which has been passed before, is reached. Naturally such a point Q must be recognisable so that some sign is necessary, perhaps the famous thread of Ariadne. At Q turn round and go back along the old path as far as a point R, from which a line runs which has not yet been used. Continue on such a virgin line until coming to an end-point or to a point already passed; then continue as before.

The reader should examine whether in this way, which can be very tedious, all the lines of the graph are used at least once. Simpler is the instruction which is ascribed to TRÉMAUX. One again supposes that one can recognise a point already passed and a line already used. One must, therefore, put suitable signs at the ends of the passages. Suppose that walking along the graph on a line PQ one has reached point Q. If it is an end-point, then one returns, i.e. goes along the line QP. If it is not an end-point and one has reached Q for the first time, then one continues along an arbitrary line QR. If one has already been at Q and if PQ has just been used for the first time, then one turns round and goes back, i.e. describing the line QP. If, however, PQ has already been used more than once, then one continues along an unused line QR. If no such line exists then one continues along a line QR which has been used once only.

One can show that in this way one walks along every line at most twice, in contrast to the given process of WIENER. The proof is given by KÖNIG. The proofs given by ARHENS, LUCAS and others are defective. KÖNIG gives another method by TARRY.

10. *Multicursal Curves*

Unicursal curves, that is curves such that a connected path exists which passes once and only once along each line, are also called

'Eulerian'. Their characteristic is that at all points an even number of lines meet, or exceptionally, that exactly two points are of odd order; these must then be chosen as starting and end-points of the path. We have already met such Eulerian lines in the Königsberg bridges problem.

Now it is immediately obvious that if one doubles up all the lines of the complex, that is if one allows each line to be covered twice, the

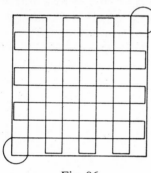

Fig. 86

line-complex becomes Eulerian, since at each point an even number of lines now meet.

It is, however, sufficient to connect the points of odd order in pairs by further lines. If there are $2n$ points of odd order then one has to insert n new lines. In the chessboard model of Fig. 86, for example, there were originally 28 points of order 3, so that 14 new lines have been inserted. The line-complex can now be covered unicursally in one closed path.

But what does one do if $2n + 1$, that is an odd number, of points of odd order occur? We show that this case is impossible. For if e_v denotes the number of points of order v, and if k is the total number of lines, then

$$e_1 + 2e_2 + 3e_3 + 4e_4 + \ldots + re_r = 2k$$

is an even number. (See p. 31.) But

$$2e_2 + 2e_3 + 4e_4 + 4e_5 + \ldots$$

is certainly also even, and so the difference of two

$$e_1 + e_3 + e_5 + \ldots$$

is even. Thus the number of points of odd order is always even.

11. *Chains*

A chain is made up of at least two closed curves (representatives of threads, wires and such like) connected to each other in such a way that it is impossible to separate them without tearing. The simplest form of chain is that which consists of two or more links, where every two consecutive links are interlocked (Fig. 87), or where many

links are interlocked with one and the same link (Fig. 88). Examples
of the first form are applied in manifold ways in engineering, but
they also occur as jewellery. An example of the second form is a
key ring with keys; other examples are the threads, worn as adorn-
ments round the throat or on the arm, on which pierced articles of
the same kind, such as pearls, corals, shells, teeth are threaded.

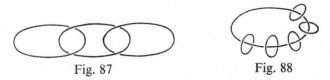

Fig. 87   Fig. 88

For the time being we will restrict ourselves to such linear structures and exclude concatenations of these things among themselves,
such as chain-mail or pendant jewellery.

The single links of the chain may be in the topological sense
circles or knots; but here again we restrict ourselves to the simplest
case, that of circles.

The two forms of chain mentioned (combinations of the two are
possible) differ from each other in the following way. If one removes
any but an end link from a chain of the first type the chain falls into
two parts. If one removes from a chain of the second type the circle
which passes through all the other links, then the chain falls completely apart into distinct links. In
contrast, if one removes one of
the 'threaded' links the other links
remain connected to the common
circle.

There is a clear distinction between the cases sketched in Figs.
89 and 91. We remind the reader
of the two-braid knot which was
shown earlier in Fig. 69. Fig. 91
gives an example which, instead

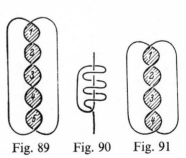

Fig. 89   Fig. 90   Fig. 91

of two shaded regions, has four. In general, such a two-braid knot is
characterised by $2n$ such regions. By the way, if in Fig. 91 one pulls
out one of the threads of the braid into a straight line, about which the
other thread now winds, and then cuts the straight thread (Fig. 90),
one has the type of twisted thread used to characterise the numbers in
the Quipu (Fig. 12).

If, instead, the two-braid is distinguished by an odd number of regions, in Fig. 89 by 5 and in general by $2n + 1$, then the connecting of the two ends does not produce a knot, but the interlacing of the two links, $(n + 1)$-times. In Fig. 89, therefore, a three-fold interlacing results and the simple chains of Figs. 87 and 88 give simple linkages.

12. *Linkages*

The trade-mark of the Krupp works is three centrally arranged, overlapping circles. If one lays two circles (threads or wires) on top of each other and interlaces a third circle with them, so that the four crossings are alternate (Fig. 92), and then removes one of the original overlapping circles, the two others are not linked. This figure of three rings so linked is the coat of arms of the BORROMAEI and one often comes across it in Italy.

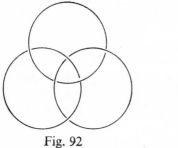 

Fig. 92   Fig. 93

This possibility does not, of course, exhaust all relationships between three linked circles. A circle C_1 can also be linked with each of the other two without these themselves being linked to each other; they then form what is usually called a chain. If one takes C_1 away then the other two circles are free. In contrast, if one removes one of the end-links of the chain then the other two links remain interlocked. Finally Fig. 93 shows a linkage of all three circles in which the removal of a circle does not leave the other two free.

Can the arrangement of three rings in Fig. 92 be generalised to a large number of rings? BRUNN has shown that one can always link n closed curves in such a way that by the removal of any one of these curves, the remaining $n - 1$ are not linked. The case which we have just had is for $n = 3$. For $n = 4$ I have taken Fig. 94 from the tract by TIETZE. Of the four curves, which are topologically equivalent to circles, one is not drawn as a circle in the metric sense. The reader should see whether he can solve the problem with four metric circles, or show that no solution is possible.

One solution of the problem for five circles is shown in Fig. 95. A fourth circle is laid over one of the set of three unlinked circles and a curve k, topologically equivalent to a circle, is passed through this aggregate of circles in such a way that all four circles are free if k is removed, and also so that the removal of any one of the four circles frees k and the other circles.

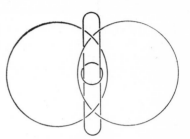

Fig. 94

If one wants to establish the result for an arbitrary number of circles one must look for a general principle in the arrangement of the circles. BRUNN has given such a principle. We now go over the cases for $n = 3, 4, 5$ again and indicate the generalisation to an arbitrary number.

We will lay down $n - 1$ concentric circles, and give an n-th closed curve k, topologically equivalent to a circle, which is linked with them. It is then obvious that if k is removed the $n - 1$ circles will be free. But one

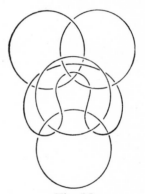

Fig. 95

must show that all the curves are freed when one removes one of the concentric circles; it will be sufficient to show that k is free (since then the other circles are necessarily free).

First we examine Fig. 96 a with the circles 1 and 2 and the curve k. To distinguish the crossings, we will put a $+$ for the case when k crosses a circle, and in the other case a $-$. Then for circle 1 we have the pattern

$$++--,$$

for circle 2 the pattern

$$+--+.$$

Now to the case $n = 4$. The circles 1, 2 and 3 in Fig. 96 b are linked by the curve k. If the first line of the pattern represents the crossings of circle 1, the second of circle 2 and the third of circle 3, then we have the pattern

$$++--$$

$$++-- \qquad --++$$

$$+--+ \qquad +--+$$

Note the symmetry in the second and third rows.

Fig. 96 c takes us straight on to the next case $n = 5$: the pattern of intersections is now:

$$++--$$

$$++-- \qquad --++$$

$$++-- \qquad --++ \qquad ++-- \qquad --++$$

$$+--+ \qquad +--+ \qquad +--+ \qquad +--+$$

Here also the symmetric construction is conspicuous. How does one continue if a fifth circle is added? The interlacing with circles 1 to 3 is not changed, only the 4th is altered. Where there was a $+$ crossing of circle 4 a mesh is inserted which has $++$ crossings with circle 4, and $+-$ crossings with circle 5; BRUNN says that the curve k 'bestrides' 5. Where there was a $-$ crossing of the circle by k, the mesh inserted there has $--$ crossings with that circle, and $-+$ crossings with 5. The reader should now write down for himself the pattern for the case $n = 6$. It is obvious how it continues for $n = 7$, etc.

We have now to show that by the removal of one of the circles the curve k is freed. We examine this

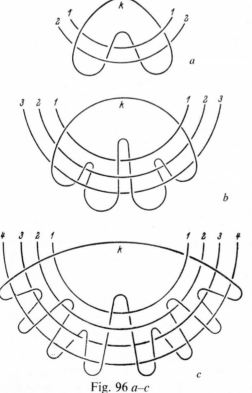

Fig. 96 a–c

in the case $n = 5$ (Fig. 96 c); it should then be clear for the general case.

If one takes circle 4 away then it is immediately obvious that one can fold the meshes upwards, either at the back or the front, so that circle 3 is also freed. Once this is done, one can do the same with circle 2 and finally also with circle 1.

If one takes circle 3 away first then all the bestriding forms $+ -$ and $- +$ disappear. Thereby circle 4 is freed and then, as before, circles 2 and 1.

If one first removes circle 2 and thereby removes its bestriding forms, then the bestriding forms which hinder the freeing of circle 3 and 4 also fall away, and these circles become free, followed by circle 1.

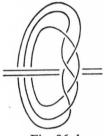

How the interlacing is undone when circle 1 is removed first, the reader can now see for himself. The immediate generalisation of the process to n circles is equally clear.

As a final word on this discussion of linkages, one further brief remark. Here also one can establish a connection with closed braids, as the reference to the two-braid has already

Fig. 96 d

shown. The linkage of three circles so that, after the removal of any one, two are separated produces a wreath as in Fig. 96 d. The corresponding expression is $(s_1 \cdot s_2^{-1})^3$ with $n = 3$.

13. *The Degree of a Graph*

If the number of lines of a graph meeting at any point is the same, then the graph is called regular. If the number is n, say, then it is

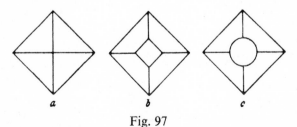

Fig. 97

called a regular graph of degree n. For example, if one projects a regular polyhedron on to a plane from a point which lies in none of the plane bounding polygons (so that no edges or vertices are lost), then the tetrahedron, cube and dodecahedron give regular graphs of third degree, the octahedron gives a regular graph of fourth degree, and the icosahedron a regular graph of fifth degree. In any graph an intersection of fourth degree can be changed into one of third degree by replacing the point at which four lines meet by a quadrilateral as in Fig. 97. In general an intersection of n-th degree can be replaced by an n-gon. Instead of a polygon, one can of course take a circle, which is topologically equivalent.

If, in a graph of third degree, one arranges that all the lines meeting at each point are marked differently—say, by colours—then one can dismantle the graph into three graphs of first degree; they are called

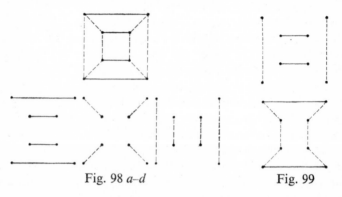

Fig. 98 *a–d*   Fig. 99

factors of the first graph. This has been done in Fig. 98 to the projection of the cube. Each of the three graphs of first degree has the same number of points as the graph of third degree, but from each point there runs only one line. The reader should dismantle the graph of fifth degree formed by the net of an icosahedron, into five factors of first degree!

Fig. 99 shows how a graph of third degree, in this case the projection of the cube, can be broken up into a factor of second degree and one of first degree. The factor of second degree is a closed path, the factor of first degree being made up of the sides not thereby used.

The reader should choose as graph the net of a dodecahedron, which is also a graph of third degree, and dismantle it into three factors of first degree, and, also, into a closed factor of second degree and one of first degree. This last factorisation can be done in three different ways.

14. *Intersection and Bridges*

Figs. 100 and 101 show two simple graphs of fourth degree of which Fig. 101 is the net of an octahedron. One can see from the drawing the decomposition of each into two factors of second degree, but these are not the only possibilities. In general every regular graph of even degree can be split up into factors of second degree. Thus it follows, for example: if in a group of people each one has exactly $2n$ acquaintances, the group can be so seated around a certain number of tables, that each one has acquaintances as neigh-

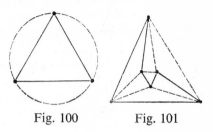

Fig. 100   Fig. 101

bours. It is possible to do this in n ways, so that each sits next to each one of his acquaintances exactly once.

The reader should examine the graphs obtained by taking the mid-points of the sides of the factors of the decomposed graphs as points of new graphs.

If one also admits loops in graphs, that is edges which begin and end at the same point, then in certain circumstances one can get into difficulties. Should one count them as one edge or two? The decision depends on whether a graph with such loops is to be regarded as regular or not. Thus the graph represented in Fig. 102 is regular and of third degree if one counts the loop as two edges, but otherwise it is not regular. On the other hand, the graph represented in Fig. 103 can be regarded as regular of degree 4, if the loop counts as one edge.

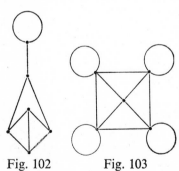

Fig. 102   Fig. 103

We choose as points of a graph the four vertices of a tetrahedron and the mid-points of two opposite edges. If we now project this spatial graph on to the plane (Fig. 104) then edges intersect, without the points of intersection counting as points of the graph. If, on the contrary, all intersections are counted as points, the graph is said to be of genus 0.[1] If one does not count

---

[1] *Tr.* See the use of genus in Chapter 1 of Part 2.

the intersection of the diagonals of the square (Fig. 103) as a point, then the graph is not of genus 0, but the graph is then regular of degree 4 or 5, depending on how one counts the loops.

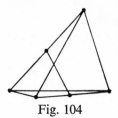

Fig. 104

If from one point of a graph to another there is only one path, and that along a single edge, then this edge is called a bridge. If this edge is removed the graph separates into two graphs, the two banks of the bridge. In a tree every line except an end-line is a bridge. In the set of graphs which have closed paths, those graphs with and without bridges can be distinguished. A bridge cannot belong to a closed path. The graph represented by Fig. 105 has two bridges, whereas the graph in Fig. 106 has none. A graph with a

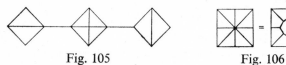

Fig. 105   Fig. 106

bridge has a division of regions such that the region which lies either side of the bridge surrounds the graph, and touches itself. Thus such an edge is not the border between two neighbouring regions. This possibility has to be excluded for certain divisions into regions.

A graph of third degree of genus 0 without bridge is also called a simple graph.

Suppose we have a graph with a bridge (Fig. 107). There are two possible ways of splitting the bridge longitudinally. In the parallel splitting of Fig. 108, a graph of

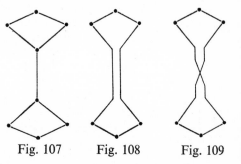

Fig. 107   Fig. 108   Fig. 109

genus 0 remains of genus 0. In the splitting with a crossing (Fig. 109) this is not the case. In both cases two points have been removed.

15. *Directed Graphs*[1]

So far the edges of a graph have not usually been distinguished by a direction. Obvious exceptions were the graphs investigated in § 6

[1] *Tr.* Alternatively, oriented graphs.

and § 7 in the discussion of ferrying and decanting. In general, one can attach a direction to the edge. For instance, if one has a polygon with a given circulation, there corresponds to it a closed graph of second degree in which the sides are cyclically directed. In a star the edges can be directed towards the centre or radiate from it or change their direction according to any other order. As is usual, we denote directed edges by arrows.

Since one also reads an arrow as 'implies', we will choose examples from logic as examples of simple directed graphs.

Let the point (1) denote: 'A polyhedron is convex', point (2): 'the characteristic of a polyhedron

$$C = e - k + f,$$

where e is the number of vertices, k the edges, f the faces, has the value 2'. Then the directed graph (1) ——→ (2) is true, but the directed graph (1) ←—— (2) is false, since (1) is a sufficient but not necessary condition for (2).

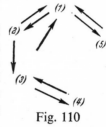

Suppose instead (1) denotes the parallel postulate, (2) the theorem that the angle sum of a triangle is two right-angles, then both (1)——→ (2) and (1) ←—— (2) are true, provided that the Archimedian axiom holds. This can also be denoted by the graph (1) ⇌ (2). (1) and (2) are equivalent.

Fig. 110

There are various possible ways of defining the conic sections. Denote by

    (1) the plane geometry definition as a geometrical locus;
    (2) the solid geometry definition as sections of a right cone;
    (3) perspective maps of the circle;
    (4) projective generation;
    (5) the real representations of the analytic form

$$ax^2 + bxy + cy^2 + dx + ey + f = 0.$$

Then the equivalence of these various definitions, as shown in the graph of Fig. 110, can be demonstrated.

16. *Infinite Graphs*

Previously we have made the assumption that the number of points and lines which make up the graphs is finite. Although we thereby leave the domain of real data, we will allow ourselves a few introductory remarks to infinite graphs. We develop these ideas from known objects.

If we mark the positive integers with zero as points on the real line then we have an infinite graph of second degree. The number of points and edges is countably infinite, as this kind of infinity is called in set theory. We can connect such 'twigs' not only to the end-points of trees, but also to any end-points or boundary points of closed graphs.

The real line with the positive and negative integers, infinite in both directions, is a further example of a graph of second degree. If one does not insist that all the edges have the same direction, which is quite natural topologically, then one has an Eulerian line. For instance, if one has a square number lattice (grid), or any other obtained from it by deformation, then there is an Eulerian line which

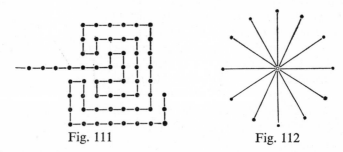

Fig. 111   Fig. 112

carries all the lattice points. This is shown in Fig. 111. One is reminded of knights' tours, although intersections occur in them; in fact one can generalise knights' tours to an infinity of squares.

Twigs and Eulerian lines are regular and of second degree. If we now take two axes intersecting at zero (as used in Cartesian geometry or in the complex plane) and as points take the integer values along the axes, then one has an infinite graph which is, however, no longer regular since the origin (zero) is of fourth degree, in contrast to all other points.

Consider a star. About the origin of a set of axes a unit circle is drawn. If we choose n equidistant points on it and join them up in order then we obtain a regular n-gon—a closed regular graph of degree 2. If, instead, we join the vertices to the centre of the circle, then we obtain the simplest regular graph of degree n (Fig. 112).[1] If one allows n to become countably infinite, then both graphs, the

[1] *Tr.* It seems that one does not count the n vertices on the unit circle as points of the graph?

closed one of order two and the star of order n, become infinite. Even if I impose the condition that the n-gons should be constructable with straight edge and compass, the number of graphs would still be infinite. If I impose the further condition that n must also be a prime number, then it is an open question whether one has an infinity of graphs; for it is unknown whether the series 3, 5, 17, 257, 65537 of prime numbers of the form $2^{(2^n)} + 1$ can be continued indefinitely; only the five mentioned are known. If, on the other hand, one requires that the co-ordinates of the points lying on the unit circle should be rational and one dispenses with the regularity of the n-gons, then the star will certainly be infinite. The condition

$$\left(\frac{p}{q}\right)^2 + \left(\frac{r}{s}\right)^2 = 1$$

or $\qquad (ps)^2 + (qr)^2 = (qs)^2$

is satisfied by an infinite number of Pythagorean number triples.

Among the trees we mentioned those which represent a dichotomy (Fig. 113), for instance a family tree in which there is no ancestor loss. I can imagine, even if not in practice, the dichotomy arbitrarily continued.

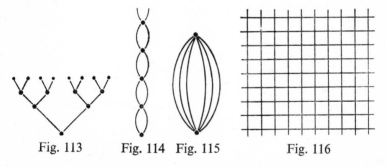

Fig. 113   Fig. 114   Fig. 115   Fig. 116

Further one can think of graphs in which two or more lines lead from one point to the next, of which simple cases are Figs. 114 and 115, which may be regarded as, say, an infinitely long two-braid and as a dipole with its lines of force, respectively.

Let us close with the square number lattice, an infinite open regular graph of fourth degree, the simplest covering of the plane without gaps (Fig. 116), which we shall refer to again in Part 2.

PART 2

The Topology of Surfaces

G

CHAPTER 1

Euler's Theorem and the Fundamental Ideas of the Topology of Surfaces

1. *Euler's Theorem for Convex Polyhedra*

IN PART 1, Chapter 6 (§ 1), we derived Euler's theorem for a polygonal net. The theorem deals with an invariant in two-dimensional space which we denoted by

$$I_2 = e - k + f.$$

A polygonal net gave the same value ($I_2 = 1$) as a single polygon;[1] thus, for example, for an n-gon $e = n, k = n, f = 1$, so that $I_2 = 1$. We made certain assumptions for the polygon and the polygonal net—assumptions which are always satisfied if the polygon and the polygonal net are convex. It is immediately obvious, however, that this condition is unnecessary. In the course of this chapter we will examine in detail which conditions are essential. For the time

Fig. 117   Fig. 118

being we just note that if we regard the four shaded quadrilaterals in Fig. 117 as a polygonal net (the net has a hole which is not counted as a quadrilateral), then we obtain the value

$$I_2 = 8 - 12 + 4 = 0$$

for I_2 and not 1.

If one applies Euler's theorem to a linear figure instead of a two-dimensional figure, then $f = 0$, but the theorem is still true, subject again to certain assumptions. Suppose we have a series of n connected line-segments on a straight line or an open line path (Fig. 118) then $e = n + 1, k = n$, so that $I_1 = 1$. Among the assumptions we must include the condition that the line path is not closed, because in that case $I_1 = 0$. We also exclude the possibility that the end lines go to infinity.

We now examine the extension of Euler's theorem to three-

[1] This was proved in 1811 by A. L. CAUCHY (1789–1857), Paris.

dimensional space, and again start with the simplest case, making assumptions which will soon be shown to be too restrictive. Suppose we have a convex polyhedron, corresponding to the case of a convex polygon in the plane. We investigate the quantity

$$I_3 = e - k + f - r$$

where r, the number of the spatial figures, has the value 1. For a rectangular solid $I_3 = 8 - 12 + 6 - 1 = 1$, and for a tetrahedron $I_3 = 4 - 6 + 4 - 1 = 1$. Is the value 1 for I_3 valid in general?

We will give a number of proofs. Project the polyhedron from a point outside it on to a plane. If, as is always possible, the point is chosen so that it does not lie in any of the planes determined by the f faces of the polyhedron, then the number of vertices, edges and faces of the polyhedron will be the same in its image in the plane. The image is made up of two polygonal nets on top of each other with a common convex contour. If we look at the polyhedron from the point of projection then one polygonal net corresponds to the front and one to the back part of the polyhedron. If the point lies very close to a surface of the polyhedron it is possible that this front surface is represented by a single polygon; this occurs, for example, if we regard Fig. 117 as the image of a rectangular solid. For the polygonal net corresponding to the front of the polyhedron $I'_2 = 1$, and equally for the other polygonal net $I''_2 = 1$. Now it does not matter if the common contour is counted twice, once for I'_2 and once for I''_2, since the number of vertices is increased by the same number as the number of edges, and so

$$I'_2 + I''_2 = 2,$$

and taking account of the fact that $r = 1$, we obtain finally

$$I_3 = 2 - 1 = 1.$$

A different approach leads more quickly to the result. We make use of the fact that in any topological investigation arbitrary deformations may take place. In counting the vertices, edges and surfaces we remove one surface for the time being. Then the closed solid becomes open and has a 'boundary'. Now the solid can be deformed at will, in particular into a plane polygonal net, for which $I_2 = 1$. If, after reversing the deformation, the surface is replaced, i.e. f is increased by 1 and remembering that $r = 1$, then we again have $I_3 = 1$.

It is easily seen that the requirement of convexity is unnecessary.

For if the polyhedron is dented in such a way that the number of vertices, edges and surfaces is unchanged, then I_3 is still 1 although the polyhedron is now not convex.

On the other hand, we can easily show by examples that I_3 is not

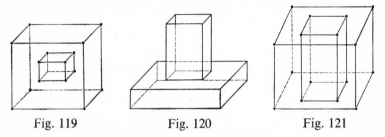

Fig. 119   Fig. 120   Fig. 121

always 1. Let the polyhedron be a rectangular solid with a similar shape removed from its interior (Fig. 119), then

$$e = 16, \qquad k = 24, \qquad f = 12, \qquad r = 1$$

so that

$$I_3 = 16 - 24 + 12 - 1 = 3.$$

Again suppose that one matchbox is stood on another and that one of the smallest surfaces of the former is identified with some part of the interior of one of the largest surfaces of the latter, the common part of the surface being removed (Fig. 120), then for the polyhedron so constructed we have

$$e = 16, \qquad k = 24, \qquad f = 11, \qquad r = 1$$

so that

$$I_3 = 16 - 24 + 11 - 1 = 2.$$

Sometimes one is surprised to find that I_3 is 1 although one expected otherwise.[1] Let the polyhedron be a rectangular solid with a rectangular prismatic hole (Fig. 121), then

$$e = 16, \qquad k = 24, \qquad f = 10, \qquad r = 1$$

and so

$$I_3 = 16 - 24 + 10 - 1 = 1.$$

Such and similar examples motivate an investigation of those properties of surfaces which are important to maintain the Eulerian

---

[1] It has been suggested that all polyhedra for which the invariant $I_3 = 1$ should be called Eulerian. But this is not suitable, for as the present example shows, a polyhedron can have two properties which individually have the effect of altering the invariant, but together cancel each other out.

invariant $I_3 = 1$, and which cause a change in this value. This is the point where our investigations really become topological.

Euler's theorem is often expressed in the form

$$e - k + f = 2 \text{ or } e + f = k + 2$$

where the value of r is omitted and only the surface of the poly-hedron is considered.[1] Since it is not essential that the vertices of a polygonal net for which $I_2 = 1$ should lie in a plane, the relation can also be expressed as follows: for an open polygonal net the invariant I has the value 1, for a closed net the value 2, assuming the necessary conditions (which still have to be investigated) are satisfied.

Instead of talking about an 'open' polygonal net one can talk about a polygonal net with one, and only one, boundary. In contrast, a closed polygonal net has no boundary. The expression

$$C = e - k + f,$$

which for a convex polyhedron and some other polyhedral forms has the value 2, is called the *characteristic* of the polyhedron.

2. *Further Proofs of Euler's Theorem*

We introduce two auxiliary quantities, the number w of all the angles appearing on the surface of the polyhedron and the sum ω of all these angles. Every edge of the polyhedron serves as the arm of four angles, two at each end. But since every angle has two arms, we have

$$w = 2k.$$

For example, the cube, which has twelve edges, has twenty-four angles.

If one projects the polyhedron on to the plane without loss of surfaces as described in § 1, then some vertices, say e_1, fall within the contour, others, say e_2, fall on the contour; thus $e = e_1 + e_2$. The e_1-vertices have an angle-sum $\omega_1 = 2\pi e_1$. The contour is an e_2-gon and has an angle-sum $(e_2 - 2)\pi$. But this angle-sum, as the contour itself, has to be counted twice; that is the angle-sum arising from the

---

[1] Euler's theorem was probably known to ARCHIMEDES. DESCARTES (1596–1650) enunciated the theorem about 1620, but this was not discovered until 1860. EULER published the result in 1752, first without proof but soon thereafter (1758) with proof. The theorem very soon appeared in the general literature and was applied principally to the derivation of the five regular polyhedra.

contour is $\omega_2 = 2(e_2 - 2)\pi$. The total angle-sum ω_k in the projected figure is thus

$$\omega_k = 2\pi(e_1 + e_2 - 2) = 2\pi(e - 2).$$

But ω_k is in fact ω, the angle-sum of the polyhedral surface; for although any individual angle is altered under the projection, every quadrilateral on the polyhedron has the same angle-sum as its projection, thus the total sum ω does not alter and $\omega = \omega_k$, i.e.[1]

$$\omega = 2\pi(e - 2) \quad . \quad . \quad . \quad . \quad . \quad . \quad (1)$$

For example, the tetrahedron has four vertices and angle-sum 4π, the cube has eight vertices and angle-sum 12π.

We now look for a second expression for ω. For a single n-gon the angle-sum is $(n - 2)\pi = n\pi - 2\pi$. We now regard n not as representing the number of vertices, but as representing the number of edges. If we take account of all the f polygons and note that each of the k edges occurs twice as the edge of a polygon, then the angle-sum of all the polygons is

$$\omega = 2k\pi - 2f\pi = 2\pi(k - f) \quad . \quad . \quad . \quad . \quad (2)$$

From (1) and (2) Euler's theorem follows, i.e.

$$e - k + f = 2.$$

Incidentally, equation (1) shows that the angle-sum of a polyhedron depends solely on the number of vertices. Even if this is immediately obvious for a plane polygon, the result for a polyhedron is nevertheless surprising.[2]

Another instructive proof of Euler's theorem is obtained if the polyhedron is projected on to a sphere instead of a plane. For simplicity take a unit sphere (i.e. a sphere of radius 1), and a point inside the polyhedron as the centre of the sphere. Project the (convex) polyhedron on to the sphere from this point, obtaining a gnomonic projection. We obtain a closed net of spherical polygons on the surface of the sphere; the image of any edge of the polyhedron is a part of a great circle.

Before we continue we quote the result that the surface area of a spherical triangle is ϵr^2, that is ϵ on a unit sphere, where ϵ is the spherical excess. If σ is the angle-sum of the spherical triangle, then $\epsilon = \sigma - \pi$. For a spherical polygon with n sides the excess is $\sigma - (n - 2)\pi$, where σ is again the angle-sum.

---

[1] This relation was already known to DESCARTES.
[2] This proof of Euler's theorem is due to STEINER.

In a manner similar to that of the above proof, we express the sum of all the angles of the spherical polygonal net in two different ways. If ω is now this angle-sum then we have

$$\omega = 2\pi e \qquad \qquad (1)$$

Now if we regard the surface area of the unit sphere as a whole, then it is well known that the area is 4π. On the other hand we may regard the surface as made up of the individual polygonal surfaces and we can calculate the sum of the polygonal angles, which is ω, and subtract from this the

$$(n - 2)\pi = n\pi - 2\pi$$

for each polygon. The sum of the $n\pi$ is as above $2k\pi$, the sum of the 2π is $2f\pi$. Hence

$$4\pi = \omega - 2k\pi + 2f\pi$$

and it follows that

$$\omega = 2\pi(2 + k - f) \qquad \qquad (2)$$

Comparison of (1) and (2) gives Euler's theorem

$$e - k + f = 2.$$

In a third proof we shall assume that the polyhedral surface has already been gnomonically projected on to the unit sphere and perform a second projection as follows: project from a point (which is not a vertex) on the surface of the sphere on to a plane touching the sphere at the opposite pole, i.e. a stereographic projection. It transforms circles on the sphere into circles in the plane. We thus obtain an image in the plane in which all the vertices and edges of the original polyhedron appear (the edges appearing as arcs of circles), and all the surfaces except one are represented. The one surface in which the centre of projection lies appears in the plane as the border of the net of all the other surfaces and stretches to infinity in all directions. We must take account of this in a further proof of Euler's theorem for polyhedra.

In Chapter 3 we shall discuss problems in which the polygonal net is regarded as a map. With this interpretation we have here an island surrounded by a sea. The island comprises $f - 1$ surfaces, the missing surface is the sea. We regard the k edges of the polygons as dykes on our island and ask: what is the minimum number of dykes that must be breached to flood all the $f - 1$ surfaces?[1] Clearly at

---

[1] RADEMACHER and TOEPLITZ use this picture in their proof of Euler's theorem. It is related to a proof by V. STAUDT.

least $f - 1$ breaches are necessary. One could destroy more, but if, for example, both sides of a dyke are already flooded, then its destruction is needless. So we put $k_1 = f - 1$ destroyed dykes and examine the remaining structure.

To begin with one can see that this complex contains no further closed line-path. For if this were the case, the inside of this path could not be flooded. Thus, in terms of the exposition in Part 1, we have an open graph. One can go from any one point of the graph to any other along a unique path, since two different paths would imply the existence of a closed line-path and this has been excluded. Again, if one point were inaccessible from the starting point, i.e. if the graph were not connected, then we would have two islands and not one. So from any vertex there is one unbroken path to each of the other $e - 1$ vertices. We can characterise each such path by the last dyke used, so that the total k_2 of unbroken dykes is

$$k_2 = e - 1.$$

Since $k = k_1 + k_2$, we have

$$k = e - 1 + f - 1$$

or

$$e - k + f = 2.$$

3. *Applications of Euler's Theorem*

A regular convex polyhedron is bounded by congruent regular polygons and all its vertices are regular and congruent. In order to determine the number of possible regular convex polyhedra, P, we note that the sum of the angles in the faces at a convex vertex is less than $360°$. P can thus be bounded by equilateral triangles, squares and regular pentagons, but not by n-gons, where $n > 5$. For example, for the hexagon the sum of three angles is $120° \times 3 = 360°$, so that no vertex can be formed. Three, four or five equilateral triangles could form a vertex, but only three squares or pentagons; in all other cases convex vertices are impossible. It appears, therefore, that five types of P-polyhedrons are possible. Euler's theorem now shows that to each type there belongs at most one polyhedron.

Consider a polyhedron of e vertices, with triangular faces and three faces meeting at each vertex. Then

$$k = \frac{3}{2}e, \qquad f = \frac{3}{3}e = e,$$

and so
$$e - \frac{3}{2}e + e = 2$$

whence
$$e = 4, \qquad k = 6, \qquad f = 4.$$

This is the tetrahedron P_4.

When the faces of the polyhedron are triangles and four faces meet at each vertex we have
$$k = \frac{4}{2}e = 2e, \qquad f = \frac{4}{3}e,$$

so that
$$e - 2e + \frac{4}{3}e = 2,$$

$$e = 6, \qquad k = 12, \qquad f = 8.$$

This is the octahedron P_8.

When the polyhedron has triangular faces and five faces meet at each vertex then
$$k = \frac{5}{2}e, \qquad f = \frac{5}{3}e$$

so that
$$e - \frac{5}{2}e + \frac{5}{3}e = 2,$$

$$e = 12, \qquad k = 30, \qquad f = 20.$$

This is the icosahedron P_{20}.

When the polyhedron has square faces and three faces meet at each vertex then
$$k = \frac{3}{2}e, \qquad f = \frac{3}{4}e,$$

so that
$$e - \frac{3}{2}e + \frac{3}{4}e = 2,$$

$$e = 8, \qquad k = 12, \qquad f = 6.$$

This is the cube, the hexahedron P_6.

Finally when the polyhedron has regular pentagonal faces and three faces meet at each vertex then
$$k = \frac{3}{2}e, \qquad f = \frac{3}{5}e,$$

so that
$$e - \frac{3}{2}e + \frac{3}{5}e = 2,$$

$$e = 20, \qquad k = 30, \qquad f = 12.$$

This is the dodecahedron P_{12}.

The fact that these five convex regular solids actually exist can be shown by constructing them.

EUCLID in the 13th book of the *Elements,* in the section dealing with the regular polyhedra, writes: 'Further, I maintain that beside the five described solids one can construct no other solid which is bounded by equilateral and equiangular congruent figures.'

EUCLID forgets to state in his formulation that the solids must be convex. He has, therefore, overlooked the regular star-polyhedra. He has also forgotten the condition that the vertices must be assumed to be regular. If, as he does, we leave out this condition while retaining convexity, then there are five more solids. As far as I know RAUSENBERGER was the first to point them out. One can first dispose of the case in which there are vertices with three faces. Then we must have tetrahedra which can only be attached to triangular faces. Such a solid will only be convex if one tetrahedron is placed on top of another tetrahedron. This double tetrahedron is a six-faced figure.

We can now assume that there are no vertices with three faces. Suppose that there are x vertices with four faces, and y vertices with five faces. Then, since the only possible faces are triangular, we have

$$e = x + y, \qquad k = \frac{4x + 5y}{2}, \qquad f = \frac{4x + 5y}{3}.$$

It follows that

$$x + y - \frac{4x + 5y}{2} + \frac{4x + 5y}{3} = 2,$$

$$6x + 6y - 12x - 15y + 8x + 10y = 12,$$

$$2x + y = 12.$$

This has the following solutions:

$$x_0 = 6, \ y_0 = \ 0, \qquad e_0 = \ 6, \ k_0 = 12, f_0 = \ 8, \quad (1)$$
$$x_1 = 5, \ y_1 = \ 2, \qquad e_1 = \ 7, \ k_1 = 15, f_1 = 10, \quad (2)$$
$$x_2 = 4, \ y_2 = \ 4, \qquad e_2 = \ 8, \ k_2 = 18, f_2 = 12, \quad (3)$$
$$x_3 = 3, \ y_3 = \ 6, \qquad e_3 = \ 9, \ k_3 = 21, f_3 = 14, \quad (4)$$
$$x_4 = 2, \ y_4 = \ 8, \qquad e_4 = 10, \ k_4 = 24, f_4 = 16, \quad (5)$$
$$x_5 = 1, \ y_5 = 10, \qquad e_5 = 11, \ k_5 = 27, f_5 = 18, \quad (6)$$
$$x_6 = 0, \ y_6 = 12, \qquad e_6 = 12, \ k_6 = 30, f_6 = 20. \quad (7)$$

The bounding cases (1) and (7) yield the octahedron and the icosahedron.

The solid (2) arises if regular pentagonal pyramids are attached to both sides of a regular pentagon. The basis of the solid (4) is a prism whose base and top are equilateral triangles whereas the side-faces are squares. To these three squares regular pyramids with regular side-faces are attached.

One can regard the icosahedron as a doubly pentagonal 'drum' with pentagonal pyramids attached, and the octahedron as a doubly triangular drum. Correspondingly, a rectangular drum can be constructed from two squares lying in parallel planes. One square is rotated through 45° with respect to the other and every vertex is joined to each of the vertices of the opposite square. Thus twice four triangles are formed, which should be equilateral. To the squares regular pyramids with four equilateral triangular faces are added. This is the solid (5). Of the remaining cases (3) and (6), (6) does not exist. The solid (3) is more difficult to construct than the rest. We start with a circle inscribed in a trapezoid with three equal sides; the fourth will be determined later. Join the vertices of the trapezoid to the centre M of the circle. At M construct a line H_1MH_2 perpendicular to the plane of the trapezoid and such that

(i) $MH_1 = MH_2$,
(ii) H_1 and H_2 form equilateral triangles with each of the three equal sides of the trapezoid,
(iii) H_1H_2 is equal to the fourth side of the trapezoid.[1]

This forms a sort of open double-tent. Construct a second double-tent congruent to the first, then the two openings will fit together if one of the structures is rotated through 90° with respect to the other. The twelve-faced surface so formed is polyhedron (3).

4. *Euler's Theorem for Stacks of Polyhedra*

Suppose that instead of a single convex polyhedron we have a whole stack of them, for example a pile of bricks. For simplicity we shall assume that the whole stack is convex and that it has no internal holes. If such holes do exist then we assume that these also have the form of convex polyhedra. Then we can count them as polyhedra for the time being and afterwards subtract them. Some of the assumptions made are unnecessary, but are made only to simplify and clarify the problem.

We again investigate the expression

$$I_3 = e - k + f - r$$

in which r is no longer 1 but arbitrary. The investigation is analogous to the first proof of Euler's theorem for polygonal nets. The first step is to reduce the polyhedra to tetrahedra.

[1] The fulfilment of the last two conditions gives rise to a cubic equation.

We take a point in the interior of a polyhedron which is not yet a pyramid and join it to the vertices of the polyhedron. Thus instead of the single polyhedron with f faces, say, we obtain f pyramids. By this construction the number of vertices has been increased by 1, the number of edges by e, the number of faces by k, the number of solids by $f - 1$. If I' is the expression for the set of f pyramids, I for the corresponding polyhedron, then

$$I' = I + 1 - e + k - f + 1$$
$$= I + 1 - (e - k + f - 1) = I + 1 - 1 = I.$$

It follows that we can prove the invariance of the expression I for the whole collection of polyhedra by dividing each individual polyhedron into pyramids.

The second stage is to split the pyramids into tetrahedra,[1] if they are not such already. Suppose the base of a pyramid is an n-gon, where $n > 3$, then divide the base by a diagonal into two polygons one of which is a triangle. Then this diagonal and the top vertex of the pyramid determine a face and we have two pyramids one of which is a tetrahedron. The corresponding changes in the expression for I are as follows: although the number of vertices remains the same, one edge is added and two faces and one solid. These changes, however, have the total effect of leaving I unchanged.

When the second stage is completed, i.e. the stack of polyhedra is broken down entirely into tetrahedra, we proceed to the third stage. Just as in the case of the polygonal net we systematically removed the triangles of which it was composed, so here we remove the tetrahedra and examine the consequent changes in the expression for I. There are the following possibilities: the tetrahedron which we remove is joined to the stack

1. by one vertex. Then 3 vertices, 6 edges, 4 faces, and 1 solid are removed; but
$$3 - 6 + 4 - 1 = 0;$$

2. by one edge. Then 2 vertices, 5 edges, 4 faces and 1 solid are removed; but
$$2 - 5 + 4 - 1 = 0;$$

3. by one face. Then 1 vertex, 3 edges, 3 faces and 1 solid are removed; but
$$1 - 3 + 3 - 1 = 0;$$

---

[1] By a tetrahedron we mean a three-sided pyramid.

4. by two faces. Then no vertex, 1 edge, 2 faces and 1 solid are removed; but

$$0 - 1 + 2 - 1 = 0;$$

5. by three faces. Then no vertex, no edge, 1 face and 1 solid are removed; but

$$0 - 0 + 1 - 1 = 0$$

and so I does not change in any of the five possible cases.

Thus one can remove one tetrahedron after the other until finally only one is left, and for this one $I = 1$. It follows, therefore, that $I_3 = 1$ for the original stack of polyhedra.

For those people who can form a concept of a four-dimensional figure, we note incidentally that one can generalise from a stack of polyhedra to a four-dimensional polytope in exactly the same way as from a polygonal net to a polyhedron. If one projects a convex polytope from a point in four-dimensional space into three-dimensional space in such a way that none of the polyhedra bounding the polytope are lost (thereby losing no faces, edges or vertices), then one obtains a double covering of the three-dimensional space by two stacks of polyhedra connected along a polyhedral contour. For each stack $I_3 = 1$ and so

$$I'_3 + I''_3 = 2$$

where I'_3 and I''_3 refer to the two stacks. But the common contour with its e_k vertices, k_k edges and f_k faces has been counted twice, so that $I_k = e_k - k_k + f_k = 2$ must be subtracted.

If one now introduces the expression

$$I_4 = e - k + f - r_3 + r_4$$

for the polytope, where r_3 denotes the number of three-dimensional polyhedra, and $r_4 = 1$ the four-dimensional polytope, then we obtain the invariant

$$I_4 = I'_3 + I''_3 - I_k + 1 = 1.$$

5. *Exceptions to the Invariant Value* 1

For simplicity, the polyhedra which we have so far examined have been assumed to be convex and then the Euler invariant

$$I_3 = e - k + f - r = 1.$$

But we noticed in § 1 that there are polyhedra for which I_3 has a different value and we shall now investigate these exceptions by way of examples.

1. We first consider the case of n discrete polyhedra, instead of a single polyhedron.[1] Then for each polyhedron we have

$$e - k + f = 2,$$

and so for the n polyhedra

$$e - k + f = 2n.$$

It follows that

$$I_3 = e - k + f - r = n.$$

From now on we shall denote the characteristic $e - k + f$ by C; then the above expression can also be written in the form

$$C = 2 + 2(n - 1).$$

Now instead of considering $n - 1$ polyhedra external to an n-th polyhedron the $n - 1$ could be internal to the polyhedron and separated from each other, i.e. appearing as discrete holes or cavities. Their characteristic is unaltered and so C will also have the same value. If now we denote the number $n - 1$ of holes by l, then for a polyhedron with l polyhedral holes (which, for simplicity, we shall for the time being take to be convex) we obtain the characteristic

$$C = 2 + 2l.$$

This agrees with the example quoted in § 1 (a rectangular solid with a rectangular hole, i.e. $l = 1$) for which we found that $I_3 = 3$ and hence $C = 4$.

In the following paragraphs, except for the final summary, we shall assume that we are dealing with a single polyhedron without internal holes.

2. Consider as a second example the solid formed from two match-boxes (Fig. 120) which we mentioned in § 1. It is not, of course, convex, but this is not the reason that $I_3 = 2$ and not 1. For if we

---

[1] The number n of polyhedra seems to be a very trivial topological invariant. But generalising, as we do in § 7, to n discrete bodies by admitting curved surfaces, this invariant becomes quite significant. For instance, the number of chromosomes in a cell remains constant although the cell undergoes fundamental changes in structure. This can be observed on quick-motion film taken by the phase contrast method. The invariant is preserved in the reduction cell division, whereas in any other cell division instead of the chromosomes remaining the same in number, they double, in such a way that the individual cell nuclei have the same chromosome invariant after the division. The whole of heredity theory is based on this change between invariance and doubling of the chromosomes.

suppose the common face of the two matchboxes to be made of rubber and the upper box slightly raised, then four new edges are formed and the resulting solid, which is still not convex, has $I_3 = 1$, since there are four new edges but only three new faces. It seems, therefore, that the reason is that previously we had a rectangular face with a rectangular hole which, after the described deformation of the solid, became four trapezia without a hole.

It seems appropriate to use this example as the motivation for a more precise examination of the assumptions we should make about the polygonal faces of the polyhedra.

If we join n coplanar points (vertices) E_1, E_2, . . ., E_n in order by line-segments (edges) E_1E_2, E_2E_3, . . ., $E_{n-1}E_n$, E_nE_1 we obtain a

Fig. 122

general plane polygon. One can go from any one point of this line path to any other point using the line path only. In this way we would exclude the case of several discrete polygons, but this is precisely the case we had with our two matchboxes and it cannot be ignored. On the other hand, the way we constructed the polygon might well have given rise to intersecting edges, i.e. the polygon could have double points, but this possibility is in fact to be excluded. (We dealt with this case in Part I, Chapter 5, § 1.) Those polygons which we shall consider as the faces of polyhedra will be assumed to be without double points.

It is unnecessary to change a polygon with a hole into a sequence of hole-less polygons as suggested in the matchbox example. It is quite sufficient to draw a supplementary edge from one vertex of the bounding polygon to one vertex of the hole. If we have n discrete holes then n extra edges drawn in a corresponding way are sufficient. In Fig. 122 there are four holes and so four edges are drawn in. It follows that if in the polygonal faces bounding the polyhedron there are a total of n holes, then the total number of edges in the characteristic will be increased by n, so reducing the characteristic by n, giving

$$e - (k + n) + f = 2,$$

i.e. $$C = 2 + n.$$

In our example $C = 3$. We also notice that in the next example (the pierced cube, Fig. 121) there are two such polygons with holes which should cause its characteristic to be increased by 2.

3. But what change is caused by the boring? We shall assume that the change in the characteristic due to the holes in the polygons is allowed for by drawing the extra edge for each.

The solid has characteristic $C_1 = 2$ as long as we take no notice of the bored hole; if the hole is considered as a body, then it also has characteristic $C_2 = 2$. Thus

$$C_1 = e_1 - k_1 + f_1 = 2,$$
$$C_2 = e_2 - k_2 + f_2 = 2.$$

From this we construct the characteristic C with vertices $e_1 + e_2 = e$, edges $k_1 + k_2 + 2 = k$, since two holes have to be removed, faces $f_1 + f_2 - 2 = f$, whence

$$C = e - k + f = e_1 - k_1 + f_1 + e_2 - k_2 + f_2 - 2 - 2 = 0.$$

If there are g non-intersecting holes through the solid, and not a single one as above, then it is clear that

$$C = 2 - 2g.$$

4. Let us now summarise the result of the deviations from a 'normal' polyhedron (e.g. a convex polyhedron) which we have considered in 1 to 3. Suppose that the polyhedron has l internal cavities, n holes in its faces and g holes through it, then the characteristic becomes

$$C = 2 + 2l - 2g + n \quad . \quad . \quad . \quad . \quad (1)$$

This is the general expression for the characteristic of a polyhedron given by L'HUILIER.[1]

One can, however, invent polyhedra which still do not fit into this framework. Therefore, we shall list a set of restrictions. The polyhedron must be closed and continuous. It is also necessary that the following be stipulated:

1. The polyhedron has no boundary. For instance, if we take any convex polyhedron, a cube, say, and take away one of its six square faces, then the remaining structure of connected polygons has a square boundary and is no longer closed. L'HUILIER's expression for the characteristic given by expression (1) above no longer holds. The stipulation in the next paragraph also excludes this case.

2. The edge of any polygon belongs to exactly two polygons, (known as neighbouring polygons). If a square were attached to one of the edges of a cube so that it stuck out from the cube, then we would have a structure for which $l = g = n = 0$, $e = 10$, $k = 15, f = 7$. Thus the characteristic still has the value 2 required by the expression (1); nevertheless we shall exclude such cases.

[1] SIMON L'HUILIER (1750–1840) was professor of mathematics in Geneva.

H

3. Consider any two polygonal faces of the polyhedron. Then it is always possible to find a sequence of neighbouring polygons which leads from one of the two former faces to the other.

4. The polygonal faces are without double points.

5. A vertex or an edge may not lie in the interior of a polygon or an edge, nor may two vertices coincide.

For example, in Fig. 123 we have a rectangular solid from which a pyramid has been removed; one face is the base of the pyramid and its vertex lies in the opposite face. In Fig. 124, instead of the pyramid,

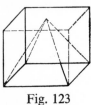 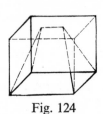

| Fig. 123 | Fig. 124 | Fig. 125 |

we have a hip-roof with its ridge lying in the surface of the poly-hedron. Although in both cases the characteristic still turns out to have the value 2 it is usual to exclude such cases and to restrict the discussion to simple polyhedra without double points.

It is also easy to make up examples of a point or line lying in a line. For instance, take a cube and attach a hip-roof to one of its faces. Then, in a similar manner to that above, cut out a pyramid (or hip-roof) with its base in the opposite face and its vertex (or ridge) coinciding with the ridge of the attached hip-roof. One thus obtains a case for which the characteristic has changed unless new assumptions are made.

Finally a case as shown in Fig. 125. This time two pyramids have been cut out of a rectangular solid, their bases in opposite faces and their vertices coincident, i.e. the solid has a double point and may be considered the limiting case between a bored and a not-bored polyhedron. If the vertices of the two cut-out pyramids were not to coincide there would be one more vertex and all would be well; the characteristic would be 2 and not 1. We have here two cycles of edges: one cycle is characterised by the fact that if $k_1, k_2, \ldots k_n$ are the edges meeting in that vertex then there exists an arrangement for which $(k_1k_2), (k_2k_3), \ldots (k_nk_1)$ determines a sequence of neigh-bouring faces. Of course, one could extend L'HUILIER's formula to cover such cases as well, but this is not usually done.

6. *Boundary, Section, Connectivity*

A finite plane polygonal net has a boundary, but the polygonal net which bounds a polyhedron is closed and has no boundary. In the following discussion (except for a final remark) we shall disregard the solid nature of the polyhedron and refer to the surface of the polyhedron only. Thus we shall be interested in the characteristic C and not in the invariant I_3. Whether or not the polygonal net is plane is now immaterial and can be ignored. One could, for instance, leave out one surface from the polygonal net of a convex polyhedron and so obtain a polygonal net with a boundary.

An open polygonal net with a hole will have two boundaries; in the simplest case this would be a polygon within a polygon, the internal one being regarded as a hole. In general, an open polygonal net with n holes has $n + 1$ boundaries. Also, instead of removing one polygon (or a connected net of polygons) from the closed polygonal net of a polyhedron, thereby obtaining one boundary, we could remove n separate polygons and obtain n boundaries. Thus closed polygonal nets of polyhedra with n holes are equivalent to open polygonal nets with $n - 1$ holes; in both cases we have n boundaries.

Previously when faced with holes in polygons we introduced edges joining the boundaries and forcibly obtained the value 2 for the characteristic. This time we shall introduce cuts.

Suppose that we have a polygonal net with just one boundary. A cut beginning and ending on the boundary separates the net into two pieces, i.e. the connectivity is destroyed by the cut.[1] If the polygonal net has two boundaries (the simplest case is a polygon with a hole) then one can cut from one boundary to the other without getting two pieces. We call such a cut a boundary-cut or cross-cut. In general one can make n cross-cuts in a polygonal net with n holes (and therefore $n + 1$ boundaries) without dividing it into pieces. In Fig. 122 four cross-cuts are made to remove four holes.

An open polygonal net which admits at most r cross-cuts without having its connectivity destroyed is called $(r + 1)$-fold connected. Thus an ordinary convex polygon or polygonal net with one boundary is once (simply) connected, whereas the perforated square of Fig. 122 admits 4 cross-cuts and is, therefore, 5-fold connected. Thus if z denotes the connectivity, then $z = r + 1$.

[1] A further essential condition must be imposed on the polygonal net, as will be seen later.

If we now turn to the closed polygonal net which forms the surface of a convex polyhedron, then we see that any cut along a closed line path divides the surface into two pieces. We shall say that the polyhedral surface has connectivity $z = 1$; this then agrees with our previous remarks since no boundary-cut is possible for a figure without

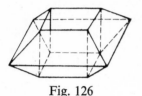

Fig. 126

a boundary. It is clear that what we have said need not be restricted to convex polyhedra, and a 'dented' polyhedron may still be simply connected.

On the other hand not all polyhedral surfaces have $z = 1$. Fig. 126 represents a polyhedron obtained from an octahedron by cutting a square channel in the direction of a diagonal. On this surface one can select a closed sequence of edges along which one can cut without dividing the surface into two pieces. It is clear that in these circumstances we cannot talk of cross-cuts (for after all there is no boundary), but rather of cuts which begin and end at the same point of the surface. We shall call such cuts regressive. Suppose now that one regressive cut has been made in the surface of Fig. 126. We now have boundaries and there exists a further sequence of edges from boundary to boundary, any one of which when cut will still not divide the surface into two pieces; any further cut, however, will so divide it. We shall say that this polyhedron which is characterised by a regressive cut and a cross-cut has connectivity $z = 3$.

The reader should show that the figures represented by Fig. 121 and Fig. 127 also have connectivity 3. Fig. 127 represents two pillars with rectangular base and roof.

In general we say that a polyhedron has connectivity z if there exist $z - 1$ cuts of the types above leaving the surface connected, and if any further such cut would separate it. The first cut will be regressive. Subsequent cuts are either regressive or begin and end at a point on a previous

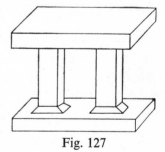

Fig. 127

cut. It is left to the reader to show that if in Fig. 127 we have n pillars then $z = -1 + 2n$.

We have shown previously that for a polyhedron with holes bored in it the characteristic $C = e - k + f$ becomes $C = 2 - 2g$. Further, the connectivity z of the polyhedral surface is related to the number g of holes in the polyhedron by the equation $z - 1 = 2g$; it follows that

$$C = 3 - z.$$

Clearly this result has been proved only for a polyhedron with holes bored in it and one must take care that all the previous limitations are obeyed. But even when they are it is still necessary to show that all other closed polyhedra can be reduced to polyhedra with holes, or equivalently, to a sequence of pillars with a common base and roof. But given such a polyhedron, then instead of examining the possible cuts, one could form the characteristic C and so obtain

$$z = 3 - C.$$

We shall call the number g of holes the genus of the polyhedron, then, for instance, a convex polyhedron has genus zero, polyhedra of the form of Figs. 121, 126, 127 have genus $g = 1$ and the solid with n pillars has genus $g = n - 1$.

To sum up: for a polyhedron without boundary with characteristic $C = e - k + f$, connectivity z, genus g, the following equations hold

$$C = 3 - z \qquad\qquad z = 3 - C$$

$$C = 2 - 2g \qquad\qquad g = 1 - \frac{C}{2}$$

$$z = 2g + 1 \qquad\qquad g = \frac{z - 1}{2}.$$

For a polygonal net with r boundaries we have

$$z = r + 1.$$

7. From Polyhedra to Curved Surfaces

It makes no difference topologically if the straight line-segments are replaced by arcs or if the plane surfaces are replaced by curved surfaces, but one or two points should be noted.

The numbers of edges and vertices of a polygonal face of a polyhedron are each not less than 3. If, however, we admit arcs of curves instead of straight line-segments it is possible to have two-vertex, one-vertex and no-vertex (e.g. a circle) figures. Is the characteristic still 1 for simple closed figures with such faces, where by 'simple' we mean without double points, isolated points, and so on? It is easily seen that the characteristic is in fact 1 for a two-vertex and a one-vertex figure, but not for a no-vertex figure. However, this last case

can also be made to conform to the general case by adding a point
to any no-vertex figure as we did in Part 1. Consider for example the
surface consisting of a net of two concentric circles. This would have
characteristic 0 without the added points (since $e = 0$, $k = 2$,
$f = 2$), characteristic 2 with the points, and if one joins these two
points across the circular ring by an edge (the ring has connectivity 2)
then the characteristic becomes 1.

We may now take a circle with $z - 1$ circular holes as an example
of a non-closed surface with connectivity z (a sieve with n holes has
connectivity $n + 1$). Any non-closed surface can be transformed into
this paradigm by allowable topological deformations. A funnel has
connectivity 2, an unbuttoned jacket or a pair of trousers (discounting the button-holes) has connectivity 3, a sweater connectivity 4,
and so on.

Now consider closed surfaces. Suppose that we have a polyhedron
whose net has connectivity 1, i.e. characteristic 2; the simplest case
being a convex polyhedron. Choose a point P inside the polyhedron
and a sphere surrounding P and project the polyhedron on to the
sphere from P. Then we obtain a spherical polygonal net (we used
a similar procedure earlier for one of the proofs of Euler's theorem),
which clearly also has characteristic 2. But here again we must discuss
those cases which, although impossible when the spherical polygonal
nets are obtained by projecting a polyhedron, are possible if we
consider general nets which could arise on a sphere.

Three intersecting great circles which do not pass through the same
point give rise to six vertices, twelve edges and eight triangular faces,
i.e. the characteristic is 2. But what if we had two-vertex, one-vertex
or no-vertex figures? If two circles intersect we have two vertices,
four edges and four faces giving characteristic 2. Equally if we join
two points by two arcs on the sphere, which is also a two-vertex
figure, we have $e = 2$, $k = 2$, $f = 2$ and so $C = 2$. Finally consider
a point on the sphere and a curve beginning and ending at this point,
then $e = 1$, $k = 1$, $f = 2$ and so once again $C = 2$. There are two
other cases on a sphere (the circles are 'pointed' as usual): the first
is the case of a single circle for which $e = 1$, $k = 1$, $f = 2$, and the
second is two non-intersecting circles for which $e = 2$, $k = 2$, $f = 3$,
but the surface lying between the two circles has connectivity 2. It
is left to the reader to consider a cylinder and a cone instead of a
sphere.

Polyhedra with characteristic 2 are called 'sphere-shaped' and
one can regard the sphere as the paradigm of closed surfaces with

connectivity $z = 1$. Every regressive cut divides any such surfaces into two pieces. All polyhedra for which $z = 1$ are topologically equivalent.[1]

Consider now the polyhedra for which $C = 0$, $z = 3$; a typical example is given by Fig. 127. A simple ring (torus) is usually taken as the paradigm of the curved solids. It can be obtained by rotating a circle about an axis which does not intersect it. This ring and the

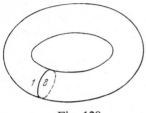

Fig. 128

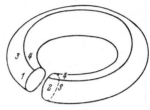

Fig. 129

two-pillared figure are clearly topologically equivalent. Since $z = 3$ there are two possible cuts. The first is a regressive cut performed in the half-plane which is bounded by the axis of rotation and which passes through one of the positions of the rotating circle (Fig. 128). The second cut is along the path described by a point on the first cut as the circle rotates (Fig. 129). Then, stretching being allowed, the surface of the torus can be flattened out into a plane rectangle with connectivity 1 (Figs. 130 and 131).

Consider next a surface with connectivity $z = 5$; we have already met a polyhedron with this connectivity, the surface of a three-pillared body. The usual paradigm of such curved surfaces is the structure represented in Fig. 132, called a double-torus. As shown in the

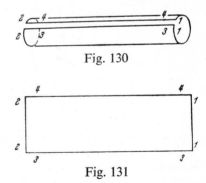

Fig. 130

Fig. 131

figure four cuts can be made without destroying the connectivity of the surface, two regressive cuts followed by two cross-cuts: any fifth cut divides the surface. In a similar way one can have 3, 4, . . . n-fold tori, and these have connectivity 7, 9, . . . $z = 2n + 1$. The torus with n holes admits n regressive cuts and n cross-cuts without

[1] The term 'homeomorphic' is also used.

the surface being separated, but any further cut would then divide it. One sometimes takes a sphere with n handles as the typical form, instead of the n-fold torus. It is easy to see that these surfaces are topologically equivalent.

A vast number of the spatial objects that one comes across in real

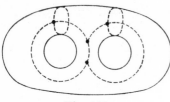

Fig. 132

life have a surface with connectivity $z = 1$; it is hardly necessary to give examples. But there are also many surfaces with $z = 3$, all rings, chain-links, pipes, nuts (for bolts), picture frames, containers with one handle, and so on. Examples of objects with higher connectivity $z = 2n - 1$ are a ladder

with n rungs, a fence with n laths and a wheel with n spokes. The usual radiator made up of n toroidal sections has connectivity $4n - 1$. It is left to the reader to consider the connectivity of the skeleton of a house, i.e. without windows and doors. On what does the connectivity depend?

One can also characterise closed surfaces by means of their genus; we did this previously for polyhedra. For a surface with connectivity $z = 2n + 1$ the genus is the number $g = n$, i.e. the number of

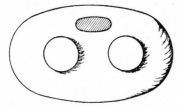

Fig. 133 a

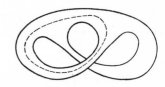

Fig. 133 b

regressive cuts which do not separate the surface. A sphere has genus 0, a ring genus 1, an n-fold torus or a sphere with n handles genus $g = n$.

By omitting one of the faces of a polyhedron the closed polygonal net without a boundary which makes up its surface becomes open with a boundary. In a similar way if one makes a hole in the surface of a sphere, a torus or a double torus (Fig. 133 a) then the new surface has a boundary; one could also introduce r boundaries in this way.[1]

---

[1] When the holes are shrunk to a point, one refers to 'pointed' surfaces.

The number r of boundaries is also characteristic of the surface. For a surface with r boundaries we have

$$z = 2g + r.$$

One can also use the characteristic C to determine the connectivity and genus of a closed surface. For instance, for the torus $e = 1$, $k = 2$ and $f = 1$, so the characteristic $C = 0$ and hence $z = 3$, $g = 1$; for the two-fold torus, where the cuts are made as shown in Fig. 132, $e = 4$, $k = 7$, $f = 1$ whence $C = -2$, $z = 5$, $g = 2$.

Consider finally two examples of a somewhat different sort. Fig. 133 b represents a surface which does not give rise to a simple (otherwise known as 'schlicht') covering of the plane, but the covering has two sheets. This pretzel-shaped surface has one boundary ($r = 1$), one regressive cut (and hence one can say that it has genus 1) and connectivity $z = 3$. As the second example take a rectangular sheet and join two opposite sides by an untwisted strip and then do the same to the other pair. How many boundaries has this structure? It is easily seen that this figure is equivalent to a simple torus.

CHAPTER 2

One-sided Surfaces

1. *The Möbius Strip*

THE OPEN belt of a man's coat or a woman's dress is a longish rectangle. If it is done up properly, then, topologically, it has the shape of a cylindrical sheet, or a circular ring if it is deformed into the plane. The belt has two edges and two sides; for instance, if the belt is made of leather one side is usually smooth and the other rough. If we have a longish rectangular piece of paper we could paint its two sides different colours, then the cylindrical sheet made with this piece of paper also has two sides coloured differently.

It is obvious that the cylindrical sheet will be cut in two by a regressive cut, i.e. a cut beginning and ending at an interior point of the surface and not meeting an edge. It is also true that a cut beginning at a point on an edge and returning to it, or to another point on the same edge, will divide the sheet in two. But a cross-cut, i.e. from a point on one edge to a point on the other, will leave the sheet in one piece.

Now it often happens when doing up a coat-belt that the belt gets unintentionally twisted through 180°. The resulting surface differs fundamentally from the one described above. The surface is called a Möbius strip or band, after the mathematician who first studied it closely.[1] It is represented in Fig. 134 geometrically simplified, i.e. without the belt-buckle (which we always ignore).

The following properties are best seen experimentally and the reader should use a model. The surface is one-sided; for take any point P and a corresponding point P' obtained by drilling a hole at P, then P and P' can be linked by a continuous curve which neither crosses an edge nor passes through the surface. Since one expects two sides one could try to colour the surface with two colours; in practice one would find one colour to be sufficient. Moreover, if the two sides of the original rectangle had already been coloured with two different colours, then these colours would now touch somewhere on the Möbius strip.

---

[1] AUGUST FERDINAND MÖBIUS (1790–1868) was professor of mathematics and astronomy at the University of Leipzig. He discussed the surface named after himself in a paper published in 1865. At about the same time LISTING also considered this one-sided surface.

The fact that the Möbius band is one-sided refers to the whole surface. Consider a point P and a sufficiently small circular neighbourhood centre P, then one can easily distinguish two sides at this point if the strip is made of paper, cloth or leather. But if the strip is considered immaterial (see § 4), as postulated in geometry, then the point on one side is identical with the point on the 'other' side.

The Möbius band, like the original rectangle and the cylinder, has a boundary. Whereas the original rectangle has only one boundary the cylinder has two; the Möbius band has only one.

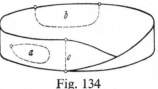

Fig. 134

Next to one of the fireplaces at Princeton University there is a lion holding an escutcheon. The escutcheon shows a fly crawling along a Möbius band; the fly is apparently proving to itself that the surface is one-sided.

Consider the possible cuts one can make in a Möbius band. There are regressive cuts beginning and ending at an interior point of the surface and cutting a piece out of it (a in Fig. 134). Then there are cuts which begin at a point on the boundary and end either at the same point or at a different one on the boundary; some such cuts also remove a piece from the surface (b in Fig. 134). Although there is only one boundary there are also cuts which run from one point to another on the boundary without the surface being separated into two parts (c in Fig. 134); the resulting surface turns out to be a rectangle which can be regarded as still twisted if one so desires. But a more remarkable cut is a regressive cut which runs parallel to the edge of the surface, i.e. begins and ends at an interior point of the surface. It does not separate the surface into two pieces, but one obtains a band which is no longer twisted through 180° but through 720° as described in an American limerick:

> *A mathematician confided*
> *That a Möbius band is one-sided,*
> *And you'll get quite a laugh*
> *If you cut one in half,*
> *For it stays in one piece*
> *When divided.*

A Möbius band was once shown to a class as a test. Even while the band was being cut 50% thought it would be a ring and as many as 20% thought it would be two rings. The band was hidden from sight after it had been cut and the class was asked how many times the new ring was twisted. Seventy per cent said it was not twisted, 20% said once twisted and 10% twice twisted. After the ring had been shown to the class again one person suggested that it was twisted three times, but although the ring was then allowed to be freely examined nobody thought it was twisted four times.[1]

The surface obtained by the above cut has, of course, two sides and two boundaries. It is not a Möbius band and a regressive cut would divide it into two pieces, both of which would have two sides and two boundaries, i.e. neither would be a Möbius band. But again there is something remarkable for the two bands are linked.

Suppose that one cuts the Möbius band along a line parallel to the edge but instead of cutting along the middle one cuts one-third of the way across. Since the strip has only one boundary this cut will come back to its beginning after two circuits and one obtains two pieces, the one a Möbius band, the other twisted through 720°; although this cut is regressive, from and to an interior point, the two bands are linked.

The reader should consider what happens when the cut runs parallel to the edge but only one-quarter of the way across; he should

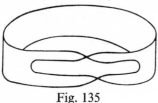

Fig. 135

then test his conclusions experimentally. Such cuts emphasise again and again that merely taking thought does not get us very far with the Möbius band; actual experiments are always necessary. I have deliberately not drawn any pictures so that the reader will pick up his scissors.

Can the idea of the Möbius band be generalised? Fig. 135 represents a band with two twisted connecting surfaces, e.g. a belt with two twisted buckle-straps. If a regressive cut parallel to the edge is made through one of the connecting surfaces we get a band which is joined to the remainder of the surface and which is twisted through 720°. Similarly one can make a regressive cut through the other connecting surface and obtain the same result. One now has a surface with three boundaries which could be transformed into a simply connected surface by two further cuts.

One can make similar cuts when the surface has n twisted connecting surfaces; this investigation is left to the reader. For instance, one could take a circular (in the topological sense) piece of paper and

---

[1] *Tr.* By a 'twist' the author means a twist through 180°.

stick to it an arbitrary number of paper strips, each by one of its ends, twist the strip through 180° and then stick the free ends on to the circular piece. We shall come across special cases in the following paragraphs.[1]

2. The Heptahedron

The Möbius band has a boundary, even if it only has one instead of the expected two. But are there also any closed one-sided surfaces?

We shall now construct a one-sided polyhedron. In Fig. 136 we have a regular octahedron, i.e. that solid which is composed of eight equilateral triangles ABC, $A'B'C'$, $AB'C$, $A'BC'$, $A'B'C$, ABC', $A'BC$, $AB'C'$: the octahedron also has three square diagonal planes $AB'A'B$, $BC'B'C$, $CA'C'A$. Choose any one of the triangular surfaces, ABC, say (shaded in Fig. 136); leave the three triangular faces touching ABC and the one opposite to it unshaded, and shade the remaining three triangles. The shaded surface then, of course, no longer forms a polyhedron. Now add to them the three square diagonal planes and examine the resulting structure. One of the three diagonal surfaces is attached to each of the three sides of the first triangle ABC; i.e. each edge of the triangle belongs to exactly two neighbouring polygons. Since the original octahedron is regular, none of the

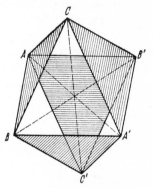

Fig. 136

bounding triangles is distinguished and so each of the other shaded triangles has the same property. It is also clear that just one triangle is joined to each of the sides of the square diagonal surfaces. It follows that this spatial structure, composed of seven surfaces, satisfies some of the set of conditions that we demanded in Chapter 1, § 4: the figure has no boundary, each edge of each polygon is attached to just two vertices, there is a path from any polygon to any other polygon across the polygonal net. But a further condition is not satisfied: the structure has double-points. Each pair of squares has a common line-segment: the double points lie on the three axes of the octahedron.

---

[1] As a passing reference we note an application of statics to one-sided surfaces which is linked with the Möbius band: F. KLEIN, *Uber Selbstspannung ebener Diagramme* (*Mathematische Annalen* 67, 1909), pp. 433 ff.

The structure, which is called a heptahedron, is a closed one-sided surface. This can be demonstrated by choosing any point on the 'outer' face (from the point of view of the observer) of the triangle ABC and then tracing a path, which always crosses an edge from one face of the heptahedron to a neighbouring face, and leads to a point which lies on the back of ABC. For example, one can cross the edge AC to the back of the square $ACA'C'$, and from there across the edge $A'C'$ to the front of $BC'A'$. Then one crosses the edge BC' to the back of the square $CBC'B'$ and finally across the edge BC to the back of the triangle ABC. Another path is from $\triangle ABC$ across the edge BC to the front of the square $CB'C'B$, across the edge $B'C'$ to the back of the $\triangle AB'C'$, across the edge AB' to the front of the square $ABA'B'$, across the edge AB to the back of the $\triangle ABC$.

Each of these paths included two of the diagonal squares. Now the axes containing the double points lie in these surfaces, so that to continue one's path across such a square an axis must be crossed, and this can only be done by breaking through one of the other squares at the point on the axis. One could, of course, object that if this is allowed, then surely it would have been much simpler to break through the original triangle, rather than make a long journey and nevertheless be forced to break through, and at more than one place instead of one.[1]

Although the polyhedron we have here is not convex, it has no boundary, no holes bored through it and no internal cavities, and all its surfaces are simply connected. What is the characteristic of such a surface? Since $e = 6$, $k = 12$ and $f = 7$ it turns out that

$$C = e - k + f = 1.$$

If we also introduce the connectivity z by means of the expression

$$C = 3 - z$$

then the heptahedron has connectivity 2. Previously, when we considered the sphere- and torus-shaped polyhedra we obtained odd values 1, 3, 5, . . . for their connectivity. The heptahedron gives us for the first time a structure which can be regarded as a polyhedron and which has an even connectivity.

There is another very natural and immediate question. The heptahedron has double points; as we have said it has three lines, the axes of the octahedron, in which the surfaces intersect. Are there

---

[1] *Tr.* There is, of course, an essential difference between the two, as the reader may readily discover.

closed one-sided polyhedra without such intersections? Could one
for instance supplement the Möbius strip (which has a boundary but
is without double points) and make it into a closed polyhedron?
The answer, which we give without proof, is no. It is very difficult
to imagine that closed one-sided surfaces can separate an inner
from an outer region without having intersections; consider, for
instance, the analogous case of a self-intersecting polygon in the
plane.

Finally, we consider the problem of constructing the net of the
heptahedron. Take a particular triangle, say *ABC*, and attach a
square to each of its sides. Then
to each of the squares, on the
sides opposite the triangle *ABC*,
attach a further triangle (Fig.
137). If we were to join up this
net without any twists then we
would obtain a triangular prism
surmounted by a triangular pyramid. But how is the heptahedron
obtained? The vertices of the net
are lettered to correspond to the
lettering of the vertices of the
heptahedron in Fig. 136. Then it
is clear that *C* must coincide with

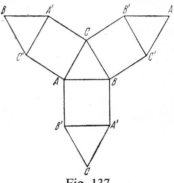

Fig. 137

C, but since the side *CA'* of the triangle is on the right and the side
CA' of the square is on the left, and similarly *CB'* is on the left in the
triangle and on the right in the square, the arm *AB'CA'B* must be
twisted through 180° before being connected up. The other arms are
connected in a similar way. We are dealing with a surface to which
three twisted strips are stuck (see the end of § 1).

If one wants to construct a model of the heptahedron, one must
overcome the difficulty arising from the intersection of the axes in the
squares. The simplest way is to cut halfway along the relevant diagonals of the squares.

Although the heptahedron is a closed polyhedron we cannot
extend our idea of genus to this one-sided surface by relating it to the
connectivity *z* using the expression

$$z = 2g + 1,$$

for *z* is an even number and so the equation has no integral solution
for *g*.

3. *The Klein Bottle*

One can examine one-sided surfaces in a different way from the above, and we shall illustrate this by considering the Möbius band. We regard the surface as made up of two sheets, one representing the front side, the other the back. The surface is therefore not simple ('schlicht'), to use an expression from the theory of functions. Now take an untwisted double-sheeted rectangle and identify the opposite edges in the following way: the left side of the upper sheet is joined to the right of the lower sheet, and the lower left to the upper right.

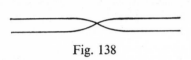

There will, of course, be a line of intersection; this is shown in the cross-section in Fig. 138.

Fig. 138

One can extend these ideas to other surfaces. For example, the surface of the torus could also be composed of an upper and a lower sheet, i.e. an outer and an inner skin. Cut open the torus with a regressive cut whose plane either passes through the axis of the torus or is at right-angles to this axis. Then one can stick the outer skin on one side of the cut to the inner skin on the other side along their circular section, and similarly the inner skin on the one side to the outer skin

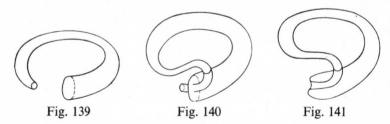

Fig. 139   Fig. 140   Fig. 141

on the other; that is, the procedure is exactly the same as with the Möbius sheet, except that the line of intersection is not a straight line but a circle. The distinction between inner and outer skin now no longer exists; the surface is one-sided.

Alternatively, one can obtain the same surface without using an inner and outer skin, as follows. Cut a torus in a plane passing through the axis and deform the resulting tube in such a way that one end has a small, and the other end a large circular section (Fig. 139). Now stretch the tube with the smaller cross-section and allow it to penetrate the wall of the larger tube and stick out through the wider opening (Fig. 140). Finally the wide and narrow tubes are joined as shown in Fig. 141. The result is a closed one-sided surface, first described by FELIX KLEIN,[1] and consequently called a Klein bottle. This closed one-sided surface has a circular curve of intersection, in contrast to the three line-segments in the heptahedron.

There is a remarkable relationship between the Klein bottle and the Möbius strip: the Klein bottle can be cut up into two Möbius strips, as the reader may see for himself. This relationship is described in an American limerick:

> *A mathematician named Klein*
> *Thought the Möbius band was divine.*
> *Said he, 'If you glue*
> *The edges of two*
> *You'll get a weird bottle like mine.'*

Another type of closed one-sided surface is associated with the handle-type paradigm among the two-sided surfaces. Fig. 142 represents a sphere with one end of a handle attached to its surface. The other end of the handle is made to penetrate the surface of the sphere and is then attached to the inner wall of the surface. One can easily convince oneself that this surface is one-sided. This type of surface can immediately be generalised by using several handles instead of one.

Fig. 142

It is easy to determine the connectivity of the Klein bottle if we examine its construction from a torus. If we take as our first cut the curve of intersection, then, after the appropriate deformation, the bottle becomes a cut torus, so that the torus and the bottle have the same connectivity $z = 3$. The same consideration will also cover the case of the handle-type figure. By the way, if anyone conjectured that all one-sided surfaces have even connectivity, taking the Möbius sheet as a precedent, then he has been disabused.[2]

The connectivity can also be deduced as follows. One can cover the bottle with a polygonal net (which should be as simple as possible) and examine the characteristic $C = e - k + f$. It turns out to be 0 and, since $z = 3 - C$, one has $z = 3$.

We tabulate the results for all those related surfaces arising from a rectangle which we have so far considered. The identifications of the sides of the rectangle are denoted by arrows and the coincident points by the same letters. It will then be clear when a twist (through

---

[1] FELIX KLEIN (1849–1925) was professor of mathematics in Erlangen, München, Leipzig, Göttingen.
[2] Since z is odd one could also talk about genus $g = 1$.

I

$180°$) is involved. The column labelled r gives the number of boundaries, the column C the characteristic, z the connectivity and s the number of sides.

Name	Schematic diagram	r	C	z	s
Rectangle		1	2	1	2
Cylinder	a← →a, b← →b	2	1	2	2
Möbius band	a← →b, b← →a	1	1	2	1
Torus	c↑ d↑, a← →a, b← →b, c↓ d↓	0	0	3	2
Klein bottle	c↑ d↑, a← →b, b← →a, c↓ d↓	0	0	3	1

4. Orientability

Consider a point P on a one-sided surface; it could be a Möbius band, a heptahedron or a Klein bottle. Suppose that there is a normal to the surface and a continuous path which leads from P to the opposite point P' without crossing the boundary. If the normal is displaced along the curve from P to P', its foot being in contact with the curve throughout, then the normal at P' has the opposite direction to that at P. This cannot happen on a two-sided surface since there is no continuous path not crossing a boundary leading from P to a point P' on the opposite side. No continuous path leads from the outside to the inside of the surface of a cube or a sphere. The path is possible, however, on a heptahedron or a Klein bottle; that is why there is no distinction between the outside and the inside.

In the previous discussion we have considered the surface, whether one-sided or two-sided, as a sort of membrane on which the points P and P' are distinct. We shall drop this conception in what follows; we maintain the distinction between one-sided and two-sidedness but regard the points P and P' as identical. Then the above result can be restated by saying that a unique normal direction can be ascribed to a point in a two-sided surface, but not to a point in a one-sided surface.

By considering a normal one has left the two-dimensionality of the surface for the three-dimensionality of the space in which it is imbedded. Can this be avoided? We again examine a continuous curve from P to P' which does not cross the boundary (if one exists). We distinguish one side of the curve at P by an arrow from P pointing to the side and we follow the curve round, continually drawing arrows pointing to the side until we come to P'. (So that the use of 'side' in the last sentence—which corresponds to its use in 'the three sides of a triangle'—is not confused with its use in 'the side of a surface', we shall use the word 'bank' instead for the former.) Then at P' the arrow has the opposite direction, and since we regard P and P' as coincident in this surface, the traversed curve has only one bank. Curves with one bank can occur only on one-sided surfaces.

In the last demonstration that the curve has one bank we remained in the surface itself and did not, as in the previous investigation, go into the surrounding space. The same is true for the following investigation. Surround the point P by a sufficiently small circle centre P in the surface. We give the circle an orientation (directional sense) and then transport it so that its centre passes along the much frequented curve PP'. Then the orientations of the circle about P and the circle about P' are not the same. Thus one-sided surfaces are not orientable.

One can arrive at the same conclusion in the following way. Draw triangles round P and P'. This could be done on a Möbius strip, for example, by choosing a transparent material (its transparency, of course, must afterwards be ignored) and by drawing the triangles covering each other. Give the triangle $\triangle p$ about P an orientation and draw a sequence of triangles leading from $\triangle p$ to the triangle $\triangle p'$ about P', each pair of neighbouring triangles touching along an edge. Now give all the triangles the same orientation, which means that the common edge will have one direction in one triangle and the opposite direction in the neighbouring triangle. Then $\triangle p$ and $\triangle p'$ will have different orientations in a one-sided surface.

Let us make this absolutely clear. On one-sided surfaces there certainly are sequences of similarly orientated triangles, beginning with $\triangle p$ and ending with a triangle about P, which are such that the two triangles about P have the same orientation. But there are also sequences in which the two triangles have a different orientation;

if the last triangle in the sequence is about P' where we consider the surface as a membrane. On the other hand this is not possible for two-sided surfaces. Consider, for instance, a triangle on an icosahedron and choose any arbitrary sequence of triangles as above. If neighbouring triangles are given the same orientation, then the orientation of the initial triangle is always the same as the final triangle.

It is clearly not essential to choose a triangular net. Let us examine the case once again, this time choosing the heptahedron which is bounded by triangles and squares. Referring to Fig. 136, we start with $\triangle ABC$ and give it the positive orientation $\overrightarrow{ABC}$. From there we go to the square $BCB'C'$ with orientation $\overrightarrow{CBC'B'}$, then to the neighbouring triangle $AB'C'$ with orientation $\overrightarrow{AB'C'}$ and from there to the square $ACA'C'$ with orientation $\overrightarrow{AC'A'C}$. Finally from there we return to the triangle ABC with orientation $\overrightarrow{ACB}$ which is the opposite orientation to the one at the beginning of the path.

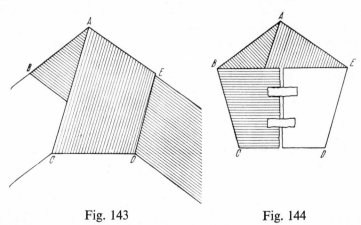

Fig. 143   Fig. 144

If one makes a knot in a strip of paper and carefully creases the knotted strip, one obtains a configuration like that shown in Fig. 143. $ABCDE$ is a regular pentagon and so the two ends of the strip form an angle of $108°$.[1] If the two ends of the strip are joined (Fig. 144) it can be seen that the strip has become twisted so that it now forms a one-sided surface. This surface is a sequence of trapezia, and this model can also be used for an instructive demonstration of the fact that a one-sided surface is not orientable.

[1] If one ties a knot in a stiff horsehair, the free ends form an angle of approximately $108°$.

The closed knot is made up of five trapezia whereas a Möbius band can be constructed from three trapezia. Consider the regular hexagon in Fig. 145. It represents a strip of paper which begins in AA' with the trapezium $AA'B'B$, is then folded backwards about BB' and continues as the trapezium $BB'C'C$, is folded forwards about CC' and ends in AA' with the trapezium $CA'AC'$. The free ends AA' and $A'A$ of the strip are stuck together. It is probable that the first thing one realises is that this closed band has only one boundary and then subsequently that it is one-sided. Since each of the trapezia is composed of three equilateral triangles, it is easily shown, using this sequence of triangles, that the band is not orientable. Starting with

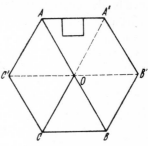

Fig. 145

$\overrightarrow{AOA'}$ we have the sequence $\overrightarrow{A'OB'}$, $\overrightarrow{B'OB}$ on the front of the first trapezium. This is followed by the sequence $\overrightarrow{BOB'}$, $\overrightarrow{COB}$, $\overrightarrow{C'OC}$ on the underside of the second trapezium. The crease in the strip now brings the third trapezium to the top and we have the sequence of triangles $\overrightarrow{COC'}$, $\overrightarrow{C'OA}$, $\overrightarrow{AOA'}$. After the crease, or rather, since the band has been stuck together at this point, after the glued edge AA', we come back to the initial triangle $\overrightarrow{A'OA}$, but on the back of the first trapezium.

There is an even simpler model of the Möbius band made up of three triangles. Choose for example three congruent equilateral triangles laid one on top of each other, $\triangle A_1B_1C_1$, $\triangle A_2B_2C_2$, $\triangle A_3B_3C_3$. Stick $\triangle A_1B_1C_1$ to $\triangle A_2B_2C_2$ by joining A_1B_1 and A_2B_2, $\triangle A_2B_2C_2$ to $\triangle A_3B_3C_3$ joining B_2C_2 and B_3C_3 and then $\triangle A_3B_3C_3$ to $\triangle A_1B_1C_1$ joining C_3A_3 and C_1A_1. Clearly it is going to be difficult to examine the inside of this collection of sticky triangles. But a path across the three glued edges leads from the upper-surface of the uppermost triangle to its under-surface. The surface is one-sided and a careful examination shows that it has only one boundary, which is formed, for example, by the sides B_1A_1, A_3C_3, C_2B_2.

A common objection that arises in the consideration we have applied to the discussion of orientability is that in the neighbourhood of a point, whether on a one- or two-sided surface, there is an outside and an inside. But the difference between the two types of surface is this: on a one-sided surface one can go from the outside to the inside without piercing the membrane (as we called it) and without crossing the boundary, if one exists. One has now to distinguish whether a curve is drawn on or in a one-sided surface. In the first case the two points which lie opposite each other on the outside and inside of the membrane are regarded as distinct, in the second case they are regarded as identical. There are also two distinct regressive cuts depending on whether one regards the cut as closed after one circuit, i.e. from P to its opposite point P' on the membrane, or after two circuits, i.e. from the point P back to the same point P.

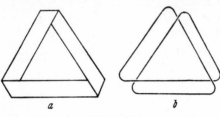

Fig. 146

Another method, which has already been described and to which we shall return in Chapter 5, is that in which the surface is replaced by two sheets. These sheets are parallel and close to each other; one sheet represents the outside and the other the inside. Then for a two-sided surface one has two independent sheets; on the other hand, for a one-sided surface, the two sheets are joined.

The surface described by Fig. 146 a is left to the reader to examine. Is it a Möbius band? Is it one-sided? In Fig. 146 b its boundary is drawn. It has only one boundary, which is topologically equivalent to an overhand knot with the free ends joined.

CHAPTER 3

Contiguous Regions

1. *The 'Neighbouring States' Theorem*

THIS THEOREM is usually introduced by the following story.[1] A man
with five sons stipulated in his will that his land was to be so divided
among his sons that every son would be a neighbour to each of his
brothers.[2] To be a neighbour meant that the land of any two brothers
was to be contiguous along a boundary line and not just at a point.
After the death of their father the brothers tried all sorts of regional
division, until eventually they had to admit that the problem had no
solution and that perhaps what their father wished to intimate to
them was that the land should not be divided.

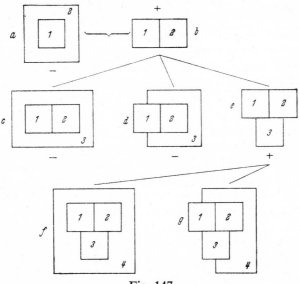

Fig. 147

Suppose now that we try this problem (Fig. 147). As representatives
of the various topologically equivalent regions we shall take rectangles. Then regions 1 and 2 are situated either as in *a*, i.e. one region
surrounding the other, or as in *b* where they are adjacent. Now con-

---

[1] W. AHRENS states that according to R. BALTZER the story is due to MÖBIUS.
[2] *Tr.* Each brother's land is, of course, to be one connected piece.

123

sider the addition of a third region 3 satisfying the stated conditions. Then case *a* cannot be used, since however the third region is added it will never be a neighbour to 1; *a* has been marked with a − sign to show that it is no longer to be considered, whereas *b*, to which the region 3 is now added, has been marked with a + sign.

There are three possibilities for region 3; it can completely surround both, one or none of the regions 1 and 2, but only in case *e* is it possible to add a fourth region in such a way that all four regions are mutually contiguous. Thus *c* and *d* are marked − and *e* +. If, as shown in *f* we draw region 4 surrounding the connected region 1, 2, 3, then the condition is satisfied, but 4 need not completely surround 1, 2 and 3; in order to satisfy the condition of the will the regions need only have a common boundary as shown in *g*.

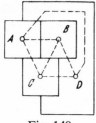

Fig. 148

If one tries to add a fifth region which will be contiguous to all the previous regions, one does not meet with much success. But such a statement is mathematically unsatisfactory and one must try to produce a proof of the impossibility. We shall do this using a method similar to the one employed in the Königsberg Bridges problem (Part I, Chapter 6, § 3). Choose a point in the interior of each region, *A* in 1, *B* in 2, *C* in 3, *D* in 4. Since 1 touches 2, 3 and 4 there are paths *AB*, *AC*, *AD* which each cross one boundary only. Similarly there exist such paths *BC*, *BD* and *CD* in regions 2, 3 and 4, and all these paths can be arranged in such a way that they do not intersect. Such a system of paths is shown in Fig. 148 which corresponds to Fig. 147 *g*.

It is clear that a similar six-path system corresponds to any configuration of four adjoining regions and conversely, to each such system of paths there corresponds a configuration of four adjoining regions.

Now suppose that we had a configuration of five regions satisfying our requirements then we could construct the corresponding system of non-intersecting paths, in which there is a path from any one region to any other. It follows, therefore, that if we can prove that such a system of paths does not exist, then an arrangement of mutually adjoining regions will also be impossible. We shall now give this proof.

The three points *A*, *B* and *C* form a triangle, for if they should by chance lie on a straight line one can always slightly displace one of the points within its domain. There are two possibilities for *D* (Fig.

149): either D lies within the triangle ABC or outside it, as for example in Fig. 148. If D is outside $\triangle ABC$ then D together with two of the points A, B, C will form a triangle (in the topological sense) and the third point will lie inside this triangle. There are no other possibilities, i.e. the configuration is always such that one of the four points (call it O) lies within the triangle PQR formed by the other three.

Now suppose that there is a fifth point E. If E is outside the $\triangle PQR$ then there can be no path to O which does not intersect one of PQ, QR, RP. So suppose E lies inside $\triangle QPR$; then it must lie in one of the triangles OPQ, OQR or ORP; let it lie in OPQ, say (we can always re-label the points as we wish). But then any path from E to R must cross one of OP, PQ, QO. In other words, in every case it is impossible to add a point E to the original system of paths and still maintain the condition that the paths

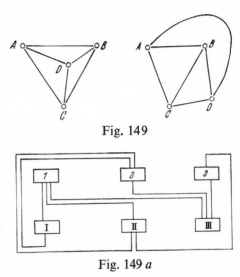

Fig. 149

Fig. 149 a

should not intersect. Since the disposal of the problem of regions is equivalent to the disposal of the path problem, we have proved the impossibility of adding a fifth region to the four regions already drawn.

Consider a different problem, known as the six-point problem. Each of the three houses 1, 2, 3 (Fig. 149 a) is to be connected to each of the opposite houses I, II, III and the paths may not cross. An attempt at a solution is shown in Fig. 149 a: 1 and 2 are connected to I, II and III, but now 3 can be joined to II and III, but not to I without crossing one of the previous paths. In fact, C. KURATOWSKI (1930) showed that there is no solution to the six-point problem.

2. *Some Extensions of the 'Neighbouring States' Theorem*

If the regions, instead of lying in a plane (or any topologically equivalent surface), lie in some other surface, can one still have only four neighbouring regions? The answer to this question is easily seen to be negative; for instance, consider the following simple example. Fig. 150 shows a set of five non-neighbouring regions if they are supposed drawn in a plane: 1 has 2, 3, 4 and 5 as neighbours but all the others have one missing. If, however, the rectangular surface is bent round into a torus in the usual way, that is opposite sides are identified, then regions 2 and 4 become contiguous and so do regions 3 and 5. There are thus more than four neighbouring regions on a torus.

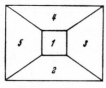

Fig. 150

Consider the question on a Möbius band. Let it be represented by a rectangle, which must be imagined twisted and with two opposite sides identified, so that in Fig. 151 the points marked a are identified as are the points marked b. Bearing this identification in mind, it is seen that the regional division shown in Fig. 151 satisfies the condition that every region adjoins every other region, i.e. we have six, and not four, contiguous regions. An even simpler division, which demonstrates the same result, is shown in Fig. 152.

It is left to the reader to investigate whether it is possible to obtain six such

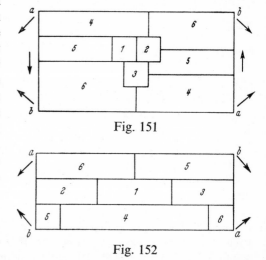

Fig. 151

Fig. 152

contiguous regions if the opposite sides of an untwisted rectangle are identified, so that one has a cylinder instead of a Möbius band.

The torus can be represented by a rectangle which has its opposite sides identified without any twist. Fig. 153 shows a torus divided into seven neighbouring regions. One could have advised the five brothers in the story of § 1 to build a bridge or dig a tunnel to connect two otherwise non-neighbouring fields. This means that topologically they would replace the plane by a torus.

These examples show that one can have at least six adjoining regions on a Möbius band and seven on a torus. That these values are also the maximum possible will be proved later, when we discuss the related problem of the minimum number of colours needed to

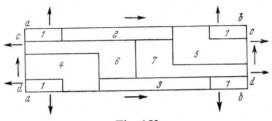

Fig. 153

colour a map in such a way that no two neighbouring states have the same colour. It is clear that at least as many colours will be needed as the maximum possible number of neighbouring states. It follows that at least six colours will be needed to colour a map on the Möbius strip and seven on the torus. But it will be shown later that six colours are sufficient for the Möbius strip and seven for the torus, so that there cannot be more than the stated number of adjoining regions on these two surfaces.

This problem can be extended into three-dimensional space. How many neighbouring regions can a spatial region have? Put differently, how many bodies can touch a given body so that any two bodies have a common face? To answer this we shall consider a structure made from children's building bricks which come in various shapes and sizes; beside the cubes there are square prisms, where the height is a multiple of the length of the side of the square. Assume that in general there are bricks whose height is n

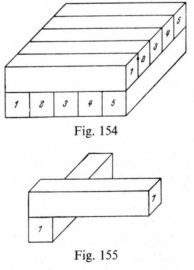

Fig. 154

Fig. 155

times as long as the side of the square end-face; in particular we have taken $n = 5$ in the figures. Lay down five blocks next to each other and running the same way: on top of them place another five blocks but running at right-angles to the first layer (Fig. 154). The blocks in the lower layer are numbered 1 to 5 from left to right, those

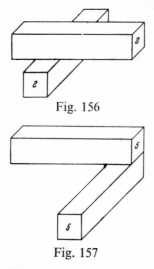

Fig. 156

Fig. 157

in the upper layer similarly but from front to back. (In general, of course, there would be n instead of five in each case.) Now construct five new solids by sticking together each pair of blocks with the same number. For instance, the new solid 1 is shown in Fig. 155, 2 in Fig. 156 and 5 in Fig. 157. It is clear by inspection that the solid 1 adjoins bodies 2, 3, 4, 5 since they all have parts of surfaces in common with 1. There is nothing particular about 1; in general we could have n such solids each neighbouring all of the others. This result is in distinct contrast to our result for the arrangement of regions in the plane. To sum up, it is possible to divide a region of space in such a way that there are an infinitely large number of bodies each of which is a neighbour to every other body.[1]

3. *The Five-colour Theorem*

Consider a map drawn either on a plane sheet of paper or on a globe. It is required to colour the countries of this map so that neighbouring states (i.e. those states with a common line frontier) have different colours. We shall prove that five colours are sufficient to do this. We choose five colours for subsequent use: blue, green, orange, red, violet. We shall refer to them by their initial letters B, G, O, R and V respectively.

Let us begin by simplifying the problem and show that the general five-colour theorem is equivalent to proving the five-colour theorem for a map, the boundaries of which form a connected regular bridgeless graph of genus 0.

If there are a number of isolated graphs (geographically speaking a number of islands in an ocean) then it is sufficient to show that each island, taking into account the surrounding ocean, can be coloured

---

[1] P. STÄCKEL proved that the number of neighbouring regions in space is infinite. Our example was given in a note by H. TIETZE. He also proved that, in contrast to the solution given here using non-convex bodies, the problem can be solved with an infinite number of convex bodies.

with five colours. Thus we can restrict ourselves to a connected region. If the island is topologically a ring with one or several holes (that is an island with internal lakes) then we count the lakes as regions. Further, the graph can be assumed to have no bridges, since if a bridge exists then the same region lies on either end of the bridge. Therefore, as far as the colouring goes, the bridge can be ignored and we have the case of two disconnected regions at either end of the bridge.

A substantial simplification in the proof is possible in that we can also assume that the boundaries of the regions form a regular graph of third degree. For if more than three countries (n, say) meet at a vertex, then we can replace the point by an n-gon or a circle so that only points of degree three remain. (This process was described on p. 78.) If now the five-colour theorem can be proved for the altered map then the inserted region can be omitted and the five-colour theorem still holds.

Finally we will show that it does not matter whether the map is on a globe or in a plane. Consider a coloured map on a globe and take a point in the interior of one of the regions. From this point we can project the map stereographically on to a plane touching the sphere at the pole opposite the centre of projection. If the five-colour theorem can be proved for the map on the globe then it is valid for the projected map on the plane and conversely. The exterior of the domain which has been divided into regions must be counted. If, for instance, we project from some point in an ocean on the terrestrial globe, we obtain a system of countries surrounded by ocean and when colouring we must colour this ocean as well. Thus in the subsequent discussion we shall assume that the map is planar, as depicted in an atlas. It does not matter whether we are dealing with the whole earth or one of the usual rectangular parts of it. In the latter case the white border around the rectangle would be regarded as the ocean.

Note that we are limiting ourselves to the case in which the map is drawn on a 'sphere-shaped' body. We exclude, for example, a torus and, in general, any surface which has a different genus from that of the sphere. If we suppose that a ring of Saturn has a tangible structure then our results will not apply to it and neither will they apply to one-sided surfaces such as the Möbius strip.

The following result, which is derived from Euler's polyhedron theorem, is of great importance here and subsequently. Consider the special polygonal net which includes its border and denote the number of faces with two edges by f_2, with three edges by f_3, . . ., with

m edges by f_m, where m is the largest number of edges of any face. Then

$$f_2 + f_3 + \ldots + f_m = f. \qquad . \quad . \quad (1)$$

Since bridges are excluded, every edge belongs to two faces and so

$$2f_2 + 3f_3 + \ldots + mf_m = 2k, \qquad . \quad . \quad (2)$$

and since three edges meet at each vertex

$$2f_2 + 3f_3 + \ldots + mf_m = 3e, \qquad . \quad . \quad (3)$$

From Euler's theorem (note that the exterior region is counted) we have

$$e - k + f = 2.$$

Multiply by 6, i.e.

$$6e - 6k + 6f = 12$$

and then from (1), (2) and (3) we obtain an equation which involves only the f; i.e.

$$4f_2 + 6f_3 + 8f_4 + 10f_5 + 12f_6 + 14f_7 + \ldots + 2mf_m$$
$$-(6f_2 + 9f_3 + 12f_4 + 15f_5 + 18f_6 + 21f_7 + \ldots + 3mf_m)$$
$$+(6f_2 + 6f_3 + 6f_4 + 6f_5 + 6f_6 + 6f_7 + \ldots + 6f_m) = 12.$$

On simplification this gives

$$4f_2 + 3f_3 + 2f_4 + f_5 - f_7 - 2f_8 - \ldots - (m - 6)f_m = 12,$$

where all the terms on the left-hand side after f_5 are negative. There are two possibilities:

(i) $m \leqslant 6$, i.e. there is no country with more than six vertices. Then $f_7, f_8, \ldots$ are all zero and so

$$4f_2 + 3f_3 + 2f_4 + f_5 = 12 \qquad . \quad . \quad . \quad . \quad (4)$$

Figs. 158 a to d give some of the simplest examples. In a there are

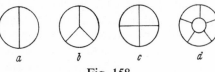

$a \qquad b \qquad c \qquad d$

Fig. 158

only two two-vertex regions, but together with the outer region we have $f_2 = 3$ and so $4f_2 = 12$. In b there are $f_3 = 3 + 1$ triangular regions, and so $3f_3 = 12$; in d we have $f_4 = 5$, $f_5 = 2$ and so $2f_4 + f_5 = 12$. In c, however, the calculation goes wrong; $f_3 = 4$, $f_4 = 1$ and $3f_3 + 2f_4 = 14$. This illustrates how important it is that all the vertices are of third degree; in the middle of this particular island four countries meet.

(ii) If there are regions with seven or more vertices, then

$$4f_2 + 3f_3 + 2f_4 + f_5 > 12 \quad . \quad . \quad . \quad . \quad (5)$$

In both cases it is clear that not all of f_2, f_3, f_4, f_5 can be simultaneously zero. One can put this otherwise; in a map in which three countries meet at any vertex, there are always countries with five or less vertices or neighbours.

After these preliminaries we will now prove the five-colour theorem by induction. The theorem is valid for a map with two, three, four or five regions: five colours would be sufficient. We suppose that the theorem has been proved for $n - 1$ regions and then prove it for n regions. We know that in the map there is at least one region which has two, three, four or five vertices. We shall prove that in each of these four cases the map with n regions can be coloured without using a new colour.

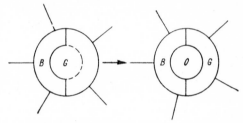

Fig. 159

Suppose that in a map with n regions there is a region with two vertices. Then in the neighbourhood of this region the map is described by Fig. 159. Remove one of the edges of the region and colour what were the surrounding two regions

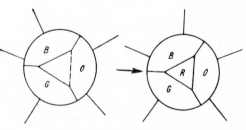

Fig. 160

with B and G say. Now we have a map of $n - 1$ regions for which we supposed the theorem proven. If the edge is now replaced then we have a choice among O, R and V for the two-vertex region. Choose O, say, and the map of n regions will be coloured with the original five colours. Now consider the case of a triangular region as described in Fig. 160. Again remove one edge temporarily and use the colours B, G and O, say. When the edge is replaced the triangular region can be coloured R. The case of a four-vertex region is similar (Fig. 161). First remove one edge and use four colours, then, when the edge is replaced we still have one colour, V, at our disposal, and all is well. But how about a pentagonal region? If we colour the five regions neighbouring the pentagon with the five colours then there is nothing left for the pentagon itself. But, in fact, four colours are sufficient since the five regions do not all touch each other (by the result of § 1). Remove the two edges which separate the

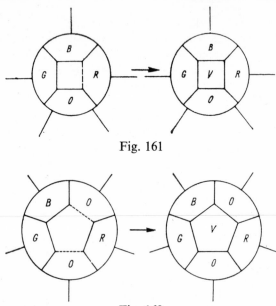

Fig. 161

Fig. 162

two similarly coloured regions from the pentagon, as shown in Fig. 162. The fact that we have reduced the number of regions by two does not matter; by the complete induction hypothesis the theorem is supposed true for all maps with $n - 1$ or less regions, and this map has $n - 2$ regions. We can, as before, replace the edges and colour the pentagon in the fifth colour.

In the above discussion, however, we have not considered one possibility. It could happen that two non-adjacent edges of the polygon under consideration might belong to the same surrounding region. This is impossible for a 2- or 3-vertex figure, but not for a 4- or 5-vertex figure. Since we are dealing with a graph of genus 0, i.e. there are no intersections, there can be only one such region in either of the two cases. For a quadrilateral one can overcome the difficulty easily (Fig. 163 a and b). If we were to remove only one edge between the quadrilateral and the region which touches it twice, then we would have a bridge. Since we excluded such a case, we remove both edges. When they are reintroduced we have two colours at our disposal for the quadrilateral.

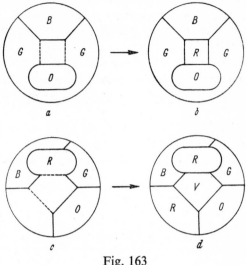

a   b

c   d

Fig. 163

In the pentagonal case one can have two disconnected regions bordering the pentagon. Delete the common two frontiers and so obtain a map with $n - 2$ regions for which the five-colour theorem is assumed to be valid. Four colours are sufficient to colour this map (Fig. 163 c), (if the region is connected then one need use only three colours). When the borders are reinstated, the fifth colour can be used for the pentagon (Fig. 163 d).

We have now completed all four possible cases and the five-colour theorem has been proved by induction.

4. *The Four-colour Problem and Chromatic Numbers*

In the previous section we showed that a map can always be coloured with five colours, whether the map is on a sphere or in a plane. We discussed how to deal with any islands which might occur and showed that one can consider all countries to have three vertices without any loss of generality.

In fact, all experience to date shows that one does not need five colours but that four are sufficient. One certainly needs four colours, and three are not sufficient, as the theorem on neighbouring regions shows. Since one state can have up to three neighbours, one must have at least four colours to distinguish them from each other.

Many mathematicians have tried to prove that four colours are sufficient in all cases. For example, P. WERNICKE worked on this early in this century, but his results were not sufficient to give a solu-

K

tion. More recently W. BRÖDEL reported briefly on a proof at the mathematical conference in Tübingen (1946). This proof employed heavy mathematical artillery, function theory and graph theory; the detailed exposition has not yet appeared.[1]

In what does the difficulty lie? To put it in a nutshell, in the necessity for colour changes. Consider the arrangement of states as shown in Fig. 164 *a* and add a fourth state to the three already coloured, *B*, *G* and *O*. Then we can use either the colour *R* or the

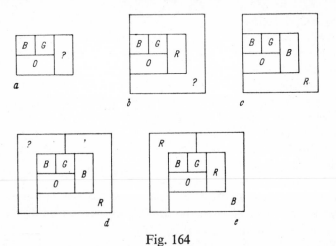

Fig. 164

colour *B* for this state. If we use *R* then we shall be in difficulties if the fifth state is situated as in Fig. 164 *b*, for none of *B*, *G* or *O* can be used. But if the colour of the fourth state is changed to *B*, then *R* is available for the fifth state (Fig. 164 *c*).

Suppose now that the fourth state had been coloured with *B* from the start, as shown in Fig. 164 *d*. Then *R* could be used for the fifth state, but one would again be in difficulties with the sixth state since none of the four colours already used would do. Thus the colour of the fourth state must be changed to *R*, the fifth state can then be coloured with *B* and the sixth with *R* (Fig. 164 *e*). Faced with the necessity of revising a previous arrangement of colours is it always possible to find a way out? To date it has always been possible; no counter-example is known, but the general proof awaits discovery.

[1] A. W. TUCKER and H. S. BAILEY report in Topology, *Scientific American*, 182 (1950), No. 1, pp. 18 ff., that the Belgian, S. M. DE BACKER (1946), has proved that four colours are sufficient if the map has less than 35 countries; the American C. N. REYNOLDS is said to have increased the number of countries to 85.

We will now consider an extension of the colouring problem, i.e. the number of colours necessary to colour a map on a surface of connectivity z. This number is often called the chromatic number: we shall look for an upper limit to it. We use the important fact that the net of state borders is a regular graph of degree three, i.e. that

$$3e = 2k$$

From Euler's theorem it follows that

$$e - k + f = 3 - z.$$

Since $e = \dfrac{2k}{3}$, this gives

$$6(f + z - 3) = 2k.$$

The number of colours needed to solve the colour problem in any given case is certainly finite since the number of faces is finite. Let n be the smallest integer which satisfies the inequality

$$nf > 6(f + z - 3), \quad \cdots \quad (1)$$

which from the above equation can also be written in the form

$$nf > 2k,$$

then we shall prove that n colours are sufficient to solve the colour problem, i.e. that at most n colours are needed. When the value of n given by the inequality is such that $f \leqslant n$ then clearly n colours are sufficient. What happens though when $f > n$? We again use induction; we suppose that the in-equality has been proved for $f - 1$ and prove that it is then valid for f.

We show first that in any map which can be coloured with n colours one face at least is bounded by less than n edges. For suppose every face were bounded by at least n edges, then there would be at least $\dfrac{nf}{2}$ edges altogether, i.e. $k \geqslant \dfrac{nf}{2}$ which is the same as $nf \leqslant 2k$.

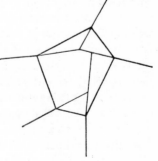

Fig. 165

But n is supposed to satisfy $nf > 2k$.
We can, therefore, find a face with at most $n - 1$ edges, and hence at most $n - 1$ neighbours: remove such a face. Then draw the neighbouring regions together to fill the hole completely, but in such a

way that no new edges are formed. How this could be done is shown in an example by Fig. 165. One must take care to make the new vertices of degree three, and this is also always possible. The new polygonal net satisfies our conditions but has one face less than the original. But for $f - 1$ faces the theorem is assumed proved, therefore the smallest n satisfying the inequality is sufficient to colour any map. We state the result again: for every z it is possible to determine an n which satisfies the inequality (1). One can therefore deduce from (1) an n such that at most n colours are necessary to colour the polygonal net.

What now is the smallest integer n which satisfies the inequality? Rewrite the inequality in the form

$$n > 6\left(1 + \frac{z-3}{f}\right).$$

If $z = 1$ or 2 then the expression tends to 6 as $f \to \infty$. Thus in both these cases, n_1 and n_2, the smallest integers satisfying the inequality, are 6. The first result is disappointing; it tells us less than we already know. The five-colour theorem has already shown us that at most five colours are necessary for a regional division when the connectivity is 1. The second result, for $z = 2$, is more encouraging. We now know that in this case at most six colours are needed, and it was shown previously (§ 2) that there is a map in which the number of neighbouring regions on a Möbius band (which has connectivity 2) is 6, i.e. that at least six colours are needed. Therefore, the colour problem for a polygonal net with connectivity 2 is solved; the chromatic number is 6.

For $z = 3$ the inequality becomes $n > 6$, i.e. $n_3 = 7$. Here again we have the solution of the colour problem. There were seven neighbouring regions on the torus. The least number of colours needed is the same as the most. Seven is therefore the chromatic number for the polygonal net with connectivity 3.

For $z > 3$ the right-hand side of the inequality decreases with increasing f. To calculate its value one must find the smallest value for f taking into account that n colours are available, i.e. $f = n + 1$. The relevant inequality is therefore

$$n > 6\left(1 + \frac{z-3}{n+1}\right).$$

This becomes

$$n(n + 1) > 6n + 6 + 6z - 18,$$
$$n^2 - 5n > 6z - 12,$$

and if we solve this quadratic inequality for n we obtain

$$n > \frac{5}{2} + \frac{1}{2}\sqrt{24z - 23}.$$

This gives the following table in which the cases previously considered are also entered:

z	1	2	3	4	5	6	7	8	9	10	11	12	13
n	6	6	7	>6·8	>7·5	>8	>8·6	>9	>9·5	>9·9	>10·3	>10·7	>11
n_z	6	6	7	7	8	9	9	10	10	10	11	11	12

Beside the cases already mentioned, empirical least numbers have been found for closed surfaces with connectivity $z = 5, 7, 9, 11$ and 13, and these numbers coincide with n_z, the largest number of colours that could be needed.

5. *The Frontier Colour Problem*

The three-colour problem for frontiers is connected with the four-colour problem for regions. Suppose that one has a regional division on a surface of genus 0, e.g. a map on the plane or on a sphere. Let the graph be regular of degree three. This time the frontiers are to be coloured and it is required that two frontiers coloured with the same colour should not meet at any vertex. Clearly this cannot be done with less than three colours. It is required to prove that three colours in fact suffice.

The difficulty here is the same as in the four-colour problem. It can happen that in the process of colouring the borders one is forced to reconsider and change some colours. Fig. 166 shows such an example; the three colours are denoted by one, two and three dashes. Suppose that in the colouring of the frontiers one has reached the state described in Fig. 166 *a*. If now a new frontier is introduced (Fig. 166 *b*), we get into difficulties

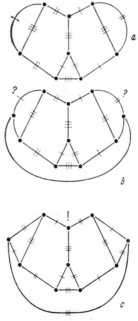

Fig. 166

κ2

at its end-points unless we retrace our steps and change the colours at the vertex marked with an exclamation mark (!) in Fig. 166 c. But what guarantee is there that such a colour change is always possible?

We shall now prove that a proof of the four-colour theorem for the regions of a map would imply a proof of the three-colour theorem for the frontiers of the same map. Let the four colours used be B = blue, G = green, O = orange, R = red, then there are six possible designations of frontiers between neighbouring countries, i.e. *BG, BO, BR, GO, GR, OR*. Mark the frontiers *BG* and *OR* with one dash — (as in Fig. 166), *BO* and *GR* with two dashes, *BR* and *GO* with three dashes, then our problem is solved. Obviously a frontier *BG* cannot meet a frontier *OR*, for if this did happen we would have four countries at this vertex which violates our assumption that each vertex is of degree three. Of course, a pre-requisite for the validity of the three-colour theorem is that the four-colour theorem has been proved.

Conversely it can be proved, although not so simply, that if the frontier colour problem were solved then the four-colour problem would also be solved. The following conjecture by TAIT is equivalent to the frontier colour problem: every bridge-less regular graph of degree three and genus 0 separates into three factors. (The various concepts, which are used here to transfer the two problems into the theory of graphs, were explained in the final paragraphs of Part I.) Expressed in terms of directed graphs the interconnection of the problem is

$$(V) \Longleftrightarrow (G) \Longleftrightarrow (T),$$

where V is the four-colour problem, G the frontier colour problem and T is TAIT's conjecture. All three problems are unsolved; if one could solve one of them then all would be solved.

We indicate without proofs an attack on T in the theory of graphs. We denote by (H_1), (H_2) and (P) the following results:

(H_1) is the lemma: In every simple graph with more than two vertices an arbitrary edge can be split in such a way that the new graph is also simple. (What splitting means is described at the end of Part I. A graph is simple if it is regular of degree three, connected and without bridges.)

(H_2) is the lemma: Every simple graph can be dismantled into two factors in such a way that two arbitrary edges lie in the factor of degree two.

(P) is PETERSEN's theorem: Every regular graph of degree three with at most one bridge is composed of two factors, one of first degree and one of second degree. A special case of this theorem is obtained if one restricts oneself to bridge-less graphs, i.e. we have the corollary (P_s): every bridge-less graph of degree three factorises into two factors.

The logical connection between these proved theorems and TAIT's conjecture is described by the following directed graph:

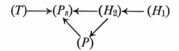

It would be sufficient if one could prove the existence of an arrow from one of (P_s), (P) or (H_2) to (T); then the other problems (V) and (G) would also be solved. Unfortunately this has not yet been achieved.

CHAPTER 4

Planes

---

1. *Tiling in the Euclidean Plane*

IN THIS chapter (as at the end of Part I) we shall not restrict our structures to being finite. In the first place we consider the plane, not merely a finite part of it, but the whole infinite plane, covered by an infinite polygonal net. We shall examine one of the many possible problems.

By the term tiling we shall mean a complete, hole-less, simple (schlicht) covering by congruent figures, where 'simple' means that no multiple coverings occur. What possible tiling patterns are there and what about the distinctive colouring of neighbouring regions? Notice, before we begin, that we shall consider only examples: the general solution of the problem of complete coverings of the plane by congruent shapes has not been obtained.

Consider the last figure in Part I (Fig. 116): the partition of the plane into squares by a square lattice. It is an infinite regular graph of degree four. Two colours are sufficient to colour neighbouring regions differently; the result is the ancient chessboard pattern which is as old as the Stone Age (Fig. 167).

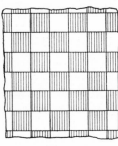

Fig. 167

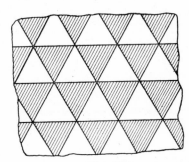

Fig. 168

Which other regular polygons can be used for tiling? First the equilateral triangle (Fig. 168), which gives a regular graph of degree six. Two colours are sufficient to colour it. This pattern also occurred in the Stone Age. The regular pentagon cannot be used because its interior angle is not a factor of 360°, but the regular hexagon can.

Then the tiling is a regular graph of degree three and needs three
colours to colour it (Fig. 169). It is the common pattern shown by a
cross-section of a honey-comb. There are, however, no other examples of tiling by regular polygons, for
the angle of an *n*-gon with $n > 6$ is
greater than 120°, and so three of these
angles cannot meet in a point. The
question of what happens to the tiling
when one admits regular polygons with
different numbers of sides has been considered, but we will not go into this. We
restrict ourselves to the case where all the
regions are mutually congruent.

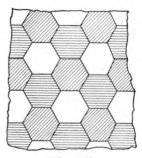

Fig. 169

In the first place we can change the
basic shapes. Instead of an equilateral
triangle we can take an arbitrary triangle; this also gives a simple
hole-less covering of the plane. (Note that the sum of the angles of
a triangle is 180°.) But Fig. 170 shows that one can also use an arbitrary quadrilateral for tiling: two colours are again sufficient. Here
the essential fact is that the angle-sum is 360°. In both cases one needs

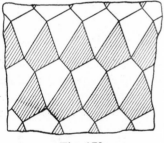

Fig. 170

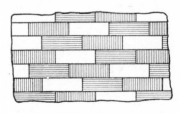

Fig. 171

more than a simple translation to bring one shape into coincidence
with its neighbour: a half-turn (reflection in a point) is also necessary. Translation alone gives the pattern of Fig. 171. Corresponding
to the covering by triangles there is a covering by parallelograms.
But with this, as with the brick-work pattern of rectangles, the
graph of fourth degree becomes a graph of third degree, and three
colours have to be used instead of two. The same happens if one
arranges the rectangles in the so-called herring-bone pattern (Fig.
172).

A final example of tiling by polygons is shown in Fig. 173. If one lays the two squares side-by-side so that two sides of the squares lie in a straight line, one obtains the so-called bride's chair with which one can tile the plane. Three colours are needed to colour this tiling by hectagons. If one covers this pattern with a square lattice 'of the same size', one obtains dissection proofs of Pythagoras' theorem by regarding the two original squares as being those on the shorter sides of a right-angled triangle. For instance, if one takes as vertices of the lattice the centres of the larger squares (shown by little circles in the figure) one obtains the so-called 'paddle-wheel' proof; on the other hand if one takes as vertices those corners of the small squares which are marked with crosses in the figure, one obtains the 'Indian'

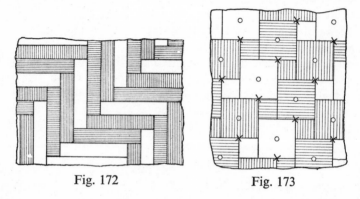

Fig. 172   Fig. 173

proof given by ANNAIRIZI. Equally, any other arbitrary position of the lattice gives rise to a dissection proof. In the special case of an isosceles right-angled triangle when the squares are equal the figure is simpler: the resulting proof for this special case is the one which PLATO lets SOCRATES obtain from the slave MENON.

So far our coverings of the plane have been made of polygonal shapes bounded by straight line-segments. It is fairly obvious that one can replace the sides of the polygons by topologically equivalent curves subject to certain conditions. For instance, in the chessboard pattern one can fix the four vertices and then deform two adjacent sides, as long as one deforms the sides opposite these two correspondingly. One can proceed similarly in the other cases.

Finally, let us consider some circular packings of the plane. The most dense packing is that in which a circle is surrounded by six circles of equal radius, each of which touches the circle in the middle and two of its neighbours. This is, of course, a covering which has holes, but not if one attaches to each circle two triangular gores (spandrels). The reader can check this experimentally and see that one such additional shape to each circle is insufficient. The pattern of the solution depends on where the gores are attached. The most common is the bull's eye pane pattern shown in Fig. 174; it is a regular graph of fourth degree. The second pattern is a regular graph of

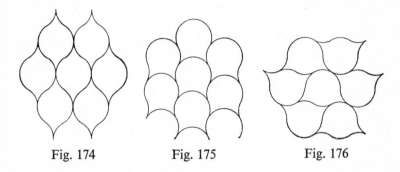

Fig. 174   Fig. 175   Fig. 176

degree three (Fig. 175). The third pattern is different from the other two in that the basic elements adjoin each other in a series of half-turns; it has points of third and fourth degree.

2. *The Projective Plane*

In Euclidean geometry we have the axiom: given a point P and a straight line g then in the plane determined by P and g there is one straight line parallel to g through the point. Whereas all other straight lines through P in the plane intersect g, there is a unique exception h, the parallel to g through P. This exception, which proves to be troublesome in the formulation of many geometrical theorems, has led to the introduction of an 'improper' point on a line; it is also called 'the point at infinity'. In spite of the difficulties this causes in a visual approach—one could ask for instance, if one introduces points at infinity, why not have two, one to the right and one to the left?—the introduction of these improper elements has proved to be very useful. Let us examine Fig. 177. A plane Γ (the object plane) is intersected by a plane B (the image plane) in a straight line a (represented on the diagram by aa, the axis). Points in the object plane are projected on to the image plane from a point Z not in Γ or B, e.g. the point P_4 in Γ is projected into the point P'_4 in the image plane. A point like P_0, which is on the axis, coincides with its image point. Let f be the line (represented in the diagram by ff) in which the plane through Z parallel to Γ meets B. We shall call this line the vanishing line, for a reason which will soon be apparent.

If a point P in the object plane describes a straight line gg then its image point P' also describes a straight line g' (represented in the diagram by $g'g'$) in the image plane; for Z and gg determine a plane which cuts the image plane in g'. Such a mapping which maps lines to lines is called a collineation. If now the point P in Γ moves off with-

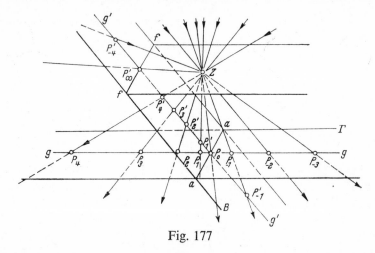

Fig. 177

out limit, then the image point approaches the vanishing line. A point P'_∞ on the vanishing line corresponds to the point at infinity, whence the line gets its name. Notice that there is just one point P'_∞ for any line gg and not two. For if instead of following the sequence of points $P_0, P_1, P_2, P_3, \ldots$ to the left, we follow the sequence $P_0, P_{-1}, P_{-2}, P_{-3}, \ldots$ to the right, then the image point does not rise from the axis to the vanishing line, but descends from the axis towards the point at infinity on g'. Then after passing this point the sequence of image points appears above the vanishing line and approaches the line from there.

This perspective mapping of a plane on to another is reciprocal: we could just as well regard B as the object plane and Γ as the image plane. If the two planes intersect then there is a vanishing line in the image plane parallel to the axis, the line of intersection of the two planes. The mapping which we carried out for the one straight line g can be carried out for any other straight line in Γ, and in each case the point at infinity will be mapped into a point on the vanishing line, i.e. the vanishing line carries the images of all the points at infinity in the object plane. Since the perspective mapping is collinear in the finite part of the plane it is natural to extend this property to the figures at infinity, the vanishing line in the image plane thus corresponds to a line at infinity in the object plane. The Euclidean plane together with the line at infinity is called the projective plane.

In the following paragraphs we shall examine the properties of the projective plane and develop finitely situated models of it, using the freedom which topological mappings allow us.

3. *The Projective Plane as a One-sided Surface*

We simplify Fig. 177 for our further investigations. Since the size of the angle between object and image plane is not significant we shall take it to be a right-angle. One can obtain all the essential information

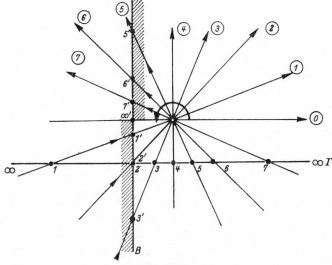

Fig. 177 *a*

by allowing the point to be projected to vary on a line *g* in Γ. Again, the position of *g* is immaterial so we shall take it as perpendicular to the axis *a*. Fig. 177 *a* shows a section of the two planes perpendicular to *a*, this section is chosen to contain *g* and its image line *g'*. We shall examine how the points of *g* are mapped on to *g'* as the projecting arrow rotates about the centre of projection.

Take the parallel to *g* directed to the right as initial position (0). The point at ∞ on *g* is mapped on to the point ∞' on *g'*. If the arrow rotates in the mathematically positive sense (i.e. anti-clockwise) to position (1), then the point 1 on g is mapped on to the point $1'$ on g', where the arrow from 1 meets the shaded left-side of g'. The arrow then rotates to position (2), where, since the point 2 lies on the axis, the corresponding point $2'$ coincides with 2. Position (3) shows that the point 3 is mapped on to $3'$, i.e. that the image point again lies on the left-hand side of g' and gets further away from the vanishing point ∞' This continues until the arrow reaches position (4), i.e.

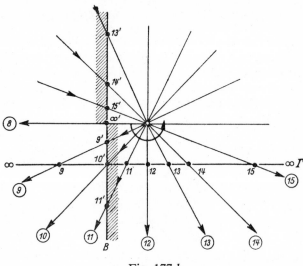

Fig. 177 b

parallel to g'. When the arrow turns further, to the position (5) say, the image point $5'$ of 5 has jumped from the bottom to the top of g', crossing the point at infinity. Moreover, it has changed from the left to the right side of g'. The positions (6) and (7) now show how the image points $6'$ and $7'$ of 6 and 7 approach the vanishing point ∞' on g' from the top, and that they always lie on the right side of g'. When the arrow is parallel to g, but this time pointing to the left, one has again reached the point ∞'. This position is denoted by (8) in Fig. 177 b, on which we shall examine the positions of the arrow as it completes its rotation. In positions (9), (10) and (11) the points 9, 10 and 11 are mapped on to $9'$, $10'$ and $11'$ on the right side of g'. After passing the point at infinity, the position being denoted by (12), the arrow maps the points 13, 14, 15 on to $13'$, $14'$, $15'$ on to the left side of g'. And so one returns to the initial position (0) of the arrow which is the mapping of the point at infinity on g on to the vanishing point ∞'.

Still referring to the object and image plane which were represented by the lines g and g' in Fig. 177 a and b, we can interpret the results of our investigation. If an arrow, pointing upwards say, moves from one end to another of a line in the object plane, then its image in the image plane moves from the vanishing point to infinity as an arrow pointing to the left, and returns to the vanishing point from the point opposite the point at infinity as an arrow directed to the right. Thus it turns out that the projective plane is a one-sided surface; a strip of the projective plane is equivalent to the Möbius band.

In the projective generation of the conics the image of a circle, which cuts the vanishing line lying in its object plane, is a hyperbola. If a point goes to infinity on one branch of the hyperbola then it returns to the finite part of the plane on the other branch, but if it left on the upper side it will return on the lower side. Only when the point has passed the point at infinity on the second branch will it again appear on top.

In order to determine the connectivity of the projective plane, we remind ourselves of the relation

$$C = 3 - z,$$

in which the characteristic

$$C = e - k + f$$

refers to the number of vertices, edges and surfaces. The projective plane is closed beyond the finite part of the plane and so boundaries are out of the question. We shall determine C.

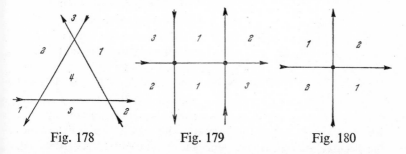

Fig. 178   Fig. 179   Fig. 180

Suppose that an octahedron lying on the plane is projected on to the plane from its centre, then we obtain a three-sided figure (Fig. 178). This figure divides the plane into four regions since we consider the plane closed at infinity; i.e. 1 and 1, 2 and 2, 3 and 3 each form one region. Since $e = 3, k = 6, f = 4$, it follows that $C = 1$ and we obtain the value 2 for the connectivity of the projective plane.

We obtain further divisions of the projective plane by placing the octahedron in different positions. Suppose the octahedron is placed symmetrically with one edge in contact with the plane and then projected from its centre: we obtain Fig. 179. Since $e = 2, k = 4, f = 3$,

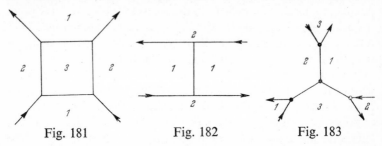

Fig. 181   Fig. 182   Fig. 183

the characteristic is again 1. If, finally, the octahedron is balanced symmetrically on one of its vertices and then projected, we obtain Fig. 180 in which $e = 1, k = 2, f = 2$, whence $C = 1$.

Figs. 181 to 183 show further examples: they are all projections of a cube from its centre. In Fig. 181 the cube has one face in contact with the plane, in Fig. 182 it is balanced symmetrically on one edge, and in Fig. 183 on one vertex. In all cases $C = 1$, which verifies that the projective plane has connectivity 2.

The reader is recommended to construct similar projections using the dodecahedron and icosahedron, and so to verify again the values we obtained for the characteristic and connectivity of the projective plane.

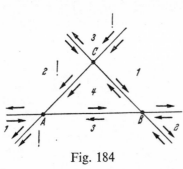

Fig. 184

The projective plane is one-sided and, therefore, not orientable. Consider Fig. 184 in which the triangle ABC is labelled region 4 and is given a mathematically positive orientation.

Region 4 has the side BC in common with region 1 which determines the orientation of the latter. Hence the orientation of 2 is determined. But now region 4, which adjoins 2 along CA, would obtain the opposite orientation to its previous one. Equally if we go from region 2 to region 3 then the orientability between 1 and 2 breaks down. Since one-sidedness is equivalent to non-orientability, we have again proved the one-sidedness of the projective plane.

4. *Finite Models of the Projective Plane*

Before we try to construct finitely situated models of the projective plane it must be pointed out that these are only models in the topological sense. In contrast to the model obtained in § 2 by a perspective mapping, we shall here preserve only the connectivity, so that any type of deformation is allowed.

In the first place we express the method of connecting up the sides of a rectangle symbolically, as we did
in the table on p.
118 for the torus,
the Klein bottle and
the Möbius band.
In Fig. 185 the
rectangle has its
sides identified as
follows: the line
segment ab is iden-
tified with $a'b'$ so
that a coincides
with a' and b with
b'; cd and $c'd'$ are
identified similarly.
Instead of a rect-
angle we could take
a regular $2n$-gon
say, in which points
symmetric with re-

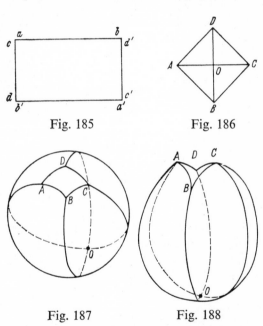

Fig. 185   Fig. 186

Fig. 187   Fig. 188

spect to its centre are identified. Equally we could identify the oppo-
site ends of the diameters of a circle, or we could take a hemisphere on which the opposite points on the bounding great circle are identified. All these figures are, of course, equivalent.

A different group of models is obtained from the projections represented in Figs. 178 to 183. If in Fig. 180 we connect the two quadrants 1 and the two quadrants 2 by strips, then in order to preserve the directional sense, these strips must each be twisted to form Möbius bands. The same holds in Figs. 181 and 182. In Figs. 178

and 183 we need three Möbius strips to achieve the same end. Three steps would also be required if we chose a hexagon instead of the rectangle of Fig. 185.

The defect of all these models is that in the construction of the actual connections by Möbius bands boundaries occur. Our next object is to find a finitely situated closed model of the projective plane.

We begin with a plane square in which AB is to be identified point-wise with CD and BC with DA (Fig. 186). To do this we deform the

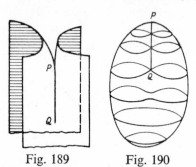

Fig. 189   Fig. 190

square into a sphere in such a way that the diagonals AC and BD become segments of great circles, whose intersection O corresponds to the intersection of the diagonals of the square. The square appears as a spherical rectangle (Fig. 187) whose sides must be properly identified. For this purpose pull the corners A and C out of the surface of the sphere as shown in Fig. 188, and join A to C in P and B to D in Q. Along the line-segment PQ so formed the surface OAB must be joined to the surface OCD and the surface OBC to the surface ODA. This means that the connection must be done cross-wise, i.e. the two pairs of surfaces intersect each other along PQ as shown in Fig. 189. The lower front sheet is connected to the upper back sheet and the lower back sheet to the upper front sheet. The resulting surface is reproduced in Fig. 190; so that the form is more easily recognisable, a sequence of sections at right-angles to PQ has been drawn.

Finally, one last question: what becomes of the colour problem on the projective plane? From the extension of the five colour theorem to surfaces of connectivity 2, we know that at most six colours are needed to colour any division into regions. If one projects the surface of a dodecahedron lying on the projective plane from its centre then one obtains the regions shown in Fig. 191. It can be seen from this figure that one in fact needs six colours. The chromatic number of the projective plane is 6.

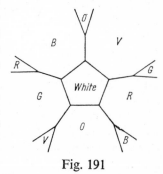

Fig. 191

5. The Boy Surface

WERNER BOY described in his thesis at Göttingen University a closed finite model of the projective plane. It looks much more complicated than those described in the previous paragraphs, but has the advantage that it possesses no singular points. In the construction of this model we follow the directions of its discoverer.[1]

We shall build the model into a rectangular system of space coordinates. Two planes at right-angles passing through the axis of a circular cylinder of radius r, divide the cylinder into four quadrants whose end-faces are quadrants of a circle. The perimeter of one of these end-faces is therefore $2r + \frac{\pi}{2}r = l$. Now take three of these circular cylinder quadrants of length l and suppose them made of plasticine, say, and lay them into the co-ordinate system so that in

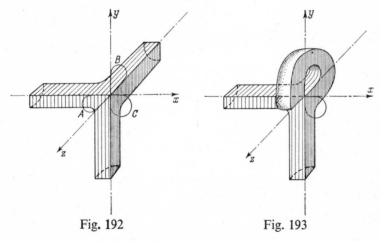

Fig. 192   Fig. 193

each case the axis of the cylinder coincides with the negative coordinate axes and runs from the origin to the point $-l$. The surfaces are so positioned that all three fall within that octant in which all three co-ordinates are negative. Their situation is depicted in Fig. 192. In this figure three end-faces A, B, C are also drawn lying in three co-ordinate planes, in such a way that the right-angles are at the origin. The circumference of the face A touches the positive z-axis

[1] A different derivation of the BOY surface, which is connected with the construction of the surfaces described in the previous paragraphs, but which uses a hexagon instead of the square used here, is given by D. HILBERT and S. COHN-VOSSEN, *Anschauliche Geometrie*, pp. 280 ff. (Springer, Berlin), 1932.

and the negative x-axis, of the face B the positive y-axis and the negative z-axis, and of C the positive x-axis and the negative y-axis.

The three quadrants of the circular cylinder are made to penetrate each other at the origin: those bits of each which lie within another are removed. The boundaries so formed are joined up and the edges and vertices are rounded off. The resulting tripodal structure has a three-fold axis of symmetry which is perpendicular to the plane $x + y + z = 0$.

Now take the cylindrical quadrant (or 'tube') which lies in the direction of the negative z-axis and bend it round so that the axis of the original cylinder takes up the position of the circumference of

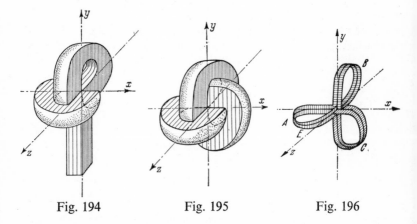

Fig. 194   Fig. 195   Fig. 196

B, and the end-face of the tube coincides with A. It is now clear why we chose a length l of cylinder. Fig. 193 describes what has happened. The tube lying in the direction of the negative x-axis is bent in a similar fashion round the A-face of the first tube so that the former's end-face coincides with C (Fig. 194). Finally, the third tube, which lies in the direction of the negative y-axis, is bent round the C-face in such a way that its end-face fits exactly on to B. This completes the BOY surface shown in Fig. 195.

In order to show the path of a regressive cut which will make the one-sidedness of the surface evident, we abandon the surface itself and examine that strip of the figure which contains the cut. We follow a normal to the surface along the cut, beginning at a point E, say, on the outside of the curve A and going towards the origin. At the origin the normal turns through a right-angle and we continue along the inside of B back to the origin. Here the normal turns through a right-angle and we pass on, on the outside of C, to the origin. The path now continues on the inside of A (thus proving the one-sidedness of the surface) back to the origin, on the outside of B to the origin, on the inside of C to the origin and finally to the outside of A where, having traversed the three loops twice each, we return to our starting point E.

CHAPTER 5

Riemann Surfaces

---

1. *Mapping by Linear Functions*

Suppose that in a functional equation of the form $y = f(x)$ we admit a complex variable instead of the real independent variable, then the dependent variable y also becomes complex. One can no longer depict the functional dependence by a curve in a plane co-ordinate system, as one does for real variables, and one must use a different method.

We shall denote the independent complex variable by $z = x + iy$ and the dependent variable by $w = u + iv$. Given two mutually perpendicular axes in the plane, we use one axis as the real axis, i.e. as base for the real numbers x, and the other as the imaginary axis, i.e. as base for the real numbers y. Then there is a one–one correspondence between the complex numbers $z = x + iy$ and the points of the so-called complex plane. Similarly there is a one–one correspondence between $w = u + iv$ and the points of another complex plane.

For some purposes it is convenient to determine the points in another way, by using a system which corresponds to polar co-ordinates just as the system in the previous paragraph corresponds to rectangular co-ordinates. Let r be the distance of a point in the (x,y)-plane (the z-plane) from the origin, ϕ the angle which this distance line-segment makes with the positive direction of the real axis, then

$$x = r \cdot \cos \phi, \qquad y = r \cdot \sin \phi,$$

whence
$$z = r(\cos \phi + i \sin \phi).$$

Then r, the absolute value of the number z (or also the modulus of the radius vector), is

$$\sqrt{x^2 + y^2}.$$

Let the corresponding values in the (u,v)-plane (the w-plane or image plane) be $u = s \cdot \cos \psi$, $v = s \cdot \sin \psi$ and hence $s = \sqrt{u^2 + v^2}$.

Consider a linear function of the form

$$w = az + b. \quad . \quad . \quad . \quad . \quad . \quad (1)$$

If $a = 1$ and $b = b_1 + ib_2$, then

$$u + iv = x + iy + b_1 + ib_2$$

and so

$$u = x + b_1, \qquad v = y + b_2.$$

This means that to an arbitrary point z in the z-plane there corresponds a point w in the w-plane which is displaced by b_1 in the direction of the real axis and by b_2 in the direction of the imaginary axis. The w-plane is derived from the z-plane by a parallel displacement characterised by b.

If $b = 0$ in (1) and a is a real number a_1, say, then

$$u + iv = a_1 x + ia_1 y,$$

and so

$$u = a_1 x, \qquad v = a_1 y,$$

i.e. if $a_1 > 1$, we have a dilatation given by a_1, and if $0 < a_1 < 1$ a contraction. Either one of these will be combined with a reflection in the origin if a_1 is negative. We shall refer briefly to all such cases as dilatations.

If in (1) $b = 0$ and a is a complex number with absolute value 1, that is of the form $\cos \alpha + i \sin \alpha$, then

$$s(\cos \psi + i \, . \, \sin \psi) = (\cos \alpha + i \, . \, \sin \alpha) \, . \, r(\cos \phi + i \, . \, \sin \phi)$$

which by a simple application of De Moivre's theorem becomes

$$s(\cos \psi + i \, . \, \sin \psi) = r \, . \, [\cos (\alpha + \phi) + i \, . \, \sin (\alpha + \phi)],$$

that is

$$s = r, \qquad \psi = \alpha + \phi.$$

Here we have a mapping of the z-plane on to the w-plane corresponding to a rotation through the angle α about the origin.

We can summarise this as follows: the complete, general linear function (1) describes a mapping of the z-plane on to the w-plane, in which a is the measure of the dilatation–rotation and b of the translation. The z-plane is topologically equivalent to the w-plane, but, more than this, the mapping is angle-preserving, for under translation, rotation and dilatation angles are preserved. Such a mapping is called conformal.

The complex plane is infinite. In order to realise its topological character better, we will map it by a one–one continuous mapping on to a finite closed surface. We take a sphere touching the complex plane at the origin and project the points of the plane on to the sphere from the pole opposite the point of contact (Fig. 197). This stereographic projection is not only one–one and continuous but also,

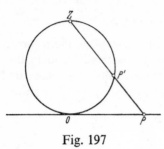

Fig. 197

although we shall not prove it here, conformal and circle-preserving, i.e. circles in the plane are mapped into circles on the sphere and vice versa. All the infinite elements of the complex plane are mapped on to the one point, the centre of projection which is the pole opposite the point of contact. It should be especially emphasised that the infinite elements of the complex plane so described are basically different from those of the projective plane. In future we shall regard the complex plane and what we derive from it as topologically equivalent to the sphere and what happens on it.

Consider a second example, the simplest rational fractional function

$$w = \frac{1}{z} \qquad \cdots \qquad (2)$$

If we again use the trigonometric form of the variables, then we have

$$s(\cos \psi + i \sin \psi) = \frac{1}{r(\cos \phi + i \sin \phi)}$$

$$= \frac{1}{r}[\cos(-\phi) + i \sin (-\phi)]$$

or $\qquad\qquad\qquad s = \frac{1}{r}, \qquad \psi = -\phi.$

The mapping defined by this function is thus representable as a 'reflection in the unit circle' and a reflection in the real axis. The interior of the unit circle in the z-plane is mapped one–one and continuously on to the exterior of the unit circle in the w-plane, and the exterior into the interior. The mapping is also conformal, but we leave this unproved. The same is true for the spheres corresponding to the two planes; circles on the spheres correspond to the unit circles in the planes. In this case also we find that the original sphere and the image sphere are topologically equivalent; corresponding to a mapping by the general linear function we obtain nothing topologically new.

2. Riemann Surfaces

The above considerations for complete linear functions and the fractional function are not sufficient when we investigate mappings of the complex plane by other kinds of functions. Consider the simplest case, the function

$$w = z^2$$

If, as before, we write

$$z = r(\cos \phi + i \sin \phi), \qquad w = s(\cos \psi + i \sin \psi),$$

then

$$s(\cos \psi + i \sin \psi) = [r(\cos \phi + i \sin \phi)]^2 = r^2(\cos 2\phi + i \sin 2\phi),$$

again using De Moivre's theorem; i.e.

$$s = r^2, \qquad \psi = 2\phi.$$

Consider the corresponding mapping of the plane. The family of concentric circles of radius r in the z-plane is mapped on to a family of concentric circles of radius $s = r^2$ in the image plane. For constant r, i.e. on any particular circle of the family, as ϕ goes from 0 to 2π (or 360°), ψ goes from 0 to 4π (or 720°). Thus corresponding to one complete circuit in the z-plane we have two complete circuits in the w-plane. This means that two points in the z-plane map to one point in the w-plane; the inverse function $z = \sqrt{w}$ is two-valued.

Fig. 198

In order to overcome this difficulty consider, instead of the single w-plane, a w-plane made up of two sheets as follows. Take two planes lying on top of each other and cut them both along the positive real axis, i.e. from 0 to ∞. Then join the four banks of the cuts cross-wise in pairs so that the sheets intersect each other. Fig. 198 shows how the left upper sheet is connected to the right lower sheet, and the right upper sheet to the left lower sheet. We obtain a connected surface composed of the two sheets. The simple circle, which was previously described twice, is now transformed into two concentric circles on top of each other, which are joined cross-wise at the cut. The images of the points $z = r(\cos \phi + i \,.\, \sin \phi)$ and $-z = r[\cos(\phi + \pi) + i \sin (\phi + \pi)]$ are now represented by points on different sheets.

The image point $w = 0$ of the point $z = 0$ is a 'singular' point; it is called a branch-point of first order. The values of the function

L

can be specified uniquely on the transformed image plane. This two-sheet structure is called a Riemann surface of two sheets, after the German mathematician BERNHARD RIEMANN (1826–1866), who decisively advanced the descriptiveness of the theory of complex functions by introducing these surfaces.

The point at infinity on the cut across which the sheets have been joined is also a branch-point, but it is not visually accessible. There-fore, we use the stereographic projection on to the sphere. Corres-ponding to the original sphere (the sphere corresponding to the z-plane) we have an image sphere of two sheets. These sheets are joined cross-wise along a meridional cut from the point of contact (of the sphere with the plane) to the opposite pole (Fig. 199). The point corresponding to $w = \infty$ is thus seen to be similar to the point corresponding to $w = 0$.

What are the topological properties of this sphere? In the first place it is two-sided. In order to determine its connectivity we

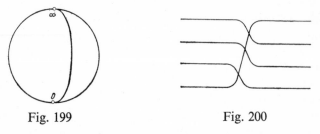

Fig. 199   Fig. 200

examine the behaviour of various regressive cuts. Any regressive cut which returns to its beginning without crossing the line in which the sheets are joined, divides the Riemann surface into two pieces. If the regressive cut crosses the join, then the cut passes from one sheet to the other and subsequently must return to the first sheet; the surface has again been divided into two pieces. The same is true if the regressive cut runs partly along the line of intersection. Thus every regressive cut divides the surface into two pieces. Consequently the connectivity $z = 1$. The relation between connectivity z and genus g was given by the expression $z = 2g + 1$; it follows that this surface has genus 0. Incidentally we could use Euler's invariant $I = e - k + f$. If we choose a 'pointed' circle on the surface, then $e = 1$, $k = 1$, $f = 2$, whence $I = 2$, and since $I = 3 - z$, the con-nectivity $z = 1$.

If instead of the quadratic function we have the function

$$w = z^n,$$

where n is a positive integer, then similar considerations lead to the following Riemann surface. The image plane is replaced by a surface with n sheets which are cut along the real axis. The corresponding sphere would likewise have n sheets cut open along the meridian between the point of contact and its opposite pole. In both cases the first sheet is joined cross-wise to the second, the second to the third, etc., the last but one to the last and finally the last to the first (Fig. 200).

This Riemann surface is two-sided, has connectivity $z = 1$ and genus $g = 0$, as similar considerations will show. A circle round the singular point described once in the z-plane would be described n times in the single image plane; the branch-point is of $(n-1)$-th order.

Consider another simple rational fractional function

$$w = z + \frac{1}{z}.$$

Using the trigonometric form for z and the arithmetic form for w, we have

$$u + iv = r(\cos \phi + i \sin \phi) + \frac{1}{r}[\cos(-\phi) + i \sin(-\phi)]$$

$$= r(\cos \phi + i \sin \phi) + \frac{1}{r}(\cos \phi + i \sin \phi),$$

whence

$$u = \left(r + \frac{1}{r}\right) \cos \phi, \qquad v = \left(r - \frac{1}{r}\right) \sin \phi.$$

Since $\sin^2 \phi + \cos^2 \phi = 1$, it follows that

$$\frac{u^2}{\left(r + \frac{1}{r}\right)^2} + \frac{v^2}{\left(r - \frac{1}{r}\right)^2} = 1.$$

Corresponding to the circle $r = $ constant in the z-plane we obtain an ellipse in the w-plane. The semi-major axis of the ellipse is $\left(r + \frac{1}{r}\right)$ and the semi-minor axis $\left(r - \frac{1}{r}\right)$.

The eccentricity becomes

$$e = \sqrt{\left(r + \frac{1}{r}\right)^2 - \left(r - \frac{1}{r}\right)^2} = \sqrt{4} = 2.$$

It follows that the family of concentric circles about the origin in the z-plane maps into a family of confocal ellipses in the w-plane.

As r increases monotonically from 0 to 1 the semi-major axis decreases monotonically from ∞ to 2, and the semi-minor axis from ∞ (the absolute value of $r - \dfrac{1}{r}$ is, of course, taken) to 0, i.e. the ellipse shrinks to the line-segment between the foci taken twice. This double line-segment corresponds to the unit circle. If r continues to increase towards ∞, the two semi-axes begin to increase again, i.e. every ellipse occurs twice.

The image of a ray $\phi =$ constant in the z-plane is the hyperbola

$$\frac{u^2}{\cos^2 \phi} - \frac{v^2}{\sin^2 \phi} = 4,$$

since $\left(r + \dfrac{1}{r}\right)^2 - \left(r - \dfrac{1}{r}\right)^2 = 4$. Corresponding to the pencil of rays we thus have a family of confocal hyperbolae, which are also confocal with the ellipses since $(2 \cos \phi)^2 + (2 \sin \phi)^2 = 4$, i.e. $e = 2$.

The mapping has been seen to be two-valued; we shall make it single valued by constructing a Riemann surface. We join two sheets cross-wise along the line-segment between the two foci which are branch-points of first order. Then the interior of the unit circle is mapped on to one sheet and the exterior on to the other sheet. Incidentally this mapping is also conformal; for instance, the ellipses and hyperbolae intersect orthogonally in the image plane, corresponding to the orthogonal intersection of the concentric circles and the pencil of rays in the z-plane.

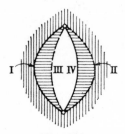

Fig. 201

If this Riemann surface is projected on to the sphere, we obtain a sphere of two sheets with two branch-points between which the sheets are joined. This structure is, however, topologically equivalent to the surface obtained for the function $w = z^2$; therefore, as with that surface, the connectivity is 1 and the genus 0. In consequence, one would expect to be able to transform this two-sheet surface into an ordinary spherical surface without tearing it. If the surface is cut open along the join we have four boundaries which we denote by I = left top, II = right top, III = left bottom and IV = right bottom; here I is to be paired with IV and II with III. These pairs are shown schematically in Fig. 201. Now it would seem obvious that to achieve our object the thing to do is to pull the inner sheet out and rejoin the sheets. This would be similar to taking a double sausage skin closed at one end and turning the inner skin inside out. But then one can only join I to III and II to IV to repair the cut, and that is contrary to our requirement. Therefore, in order to complete the transformation one would have to turn the inner sheet round, so that III and IV interchange positions and points which were adjacent before the two sheets were separated are again adjacent. Then by joining I to IV and II to III the correct connections will be made.

3. A Riemann Surface of Higher Connectivity

Consider the 'algebraic' function

$$w = \pm\sqrt{z^4 - 1}$$

or

$$w^2 = z^4 - 1.$$

The 'plus or minus' in front of the root sign suggests that we shall have a Riemann surface of two sheets.[1] Factorising the fourth degree expression under the square root sign, we get

$$w = \pm\sqrt{z - 1} \cdot \sqrt{z + 1} \cdot \sqrt{z - i} \cdot \sqrt{z + i}$$

which has the four zeros $1, -1, i, -i$. The expression is double-valued at all points of the z-plane except at these four points, which represent the fourth roots of unity. Thus the Riemann surface has four branch-points $1, -1, i, -i$.

Consider one of the linear factors $w' = \pm\sqrt{z - a}$, where a is $1, -1, +i$ or $-i$, and a continuous curve from a point z_1 to a point z_2, where z_1, z_2 and the curve all lie in one sheet. Then as z describes this curve the sign of w' remains the same, even if z_1 and z_2 coincide, i.e. the curve is closed. The curve, therefore, neither passes through the point $z = a$ nor surrounds it. To illustrate this introduce polar co-ordinates. Let the origin of co-ordinates be a, the distance of z from a be ρ, and the angle with the positive x-axis in the z-plane be ϕ, then

$$z - a = \rho(\cos\phi + i\sin\phi).$$

It follows that

$$w' = \sqrt{z - a} = \sqrt{\rho}\left(\cos\frac{\phi}{2} + i\sin\frac{\phi}{2}\right).$$

---

[1] *Tr.* In this example the z-plane (and not the w-plane) becomes a Riemann surface of two sheets.

Suppose that a lies outside the curve described by z. Then, as Fig. 202 shows, ϕ varies between the values ϕ_1 and ϕ_2 and after one circuit returns to its original value, i.e. the factor $w' = \sqrt{z - a}$ returns to its original value and z remains on the same sheet of the Riemann surface. On the other hand if a lies inside the curve (Fig. 203) ϕ

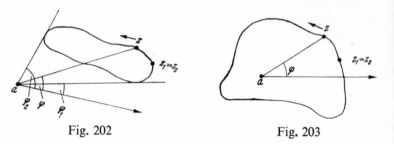

Fig. 202   Fig. 203

increases by 2π after a complete circuit. If initially, z had the value z_1

$$w' = \sqrt{z_1 - a} = \sqrt{\rho_1}\left(\cos \frac{\phi_1}{2} + i \sin \frac{\phi_1}{2}\right),$$

then after the circuit w' has the value

$$\sqrt{\rho_1}\left(\cos \frac{\phi_1 + 2\pi}{2} + i \sin \frac{\phi_1 + 2\pi}{2}\right)$$

$$= \sqrt{\rho_1}\left[\cos\left(\frac{\phi_1}{2} + \pi\right) + i \sin\left(\frac{\phi_1}{2} + \pi\right)\right]$$

$$= - \sqrt{z_1 - a}.$$

This shows that after a complete circuit of the point $z = a$, the value of w' has changed its sign and we have ended up on the other sheet of the Riemann surface. If follows that there must be a cut running from the point a, across which the sheets are to be joined. For the present it is immaterial how this cut runs; we shall decide this later.

Now there are four such factors and so the Riemann surface of two sheets for the function

$$w = \pm \sqrt{z - 1} \cdot \sqrt{z + 1} \cdot \sqrt{z - i} \cdot \sqrt{z + i}$$

will have four branch-points, at $+1$, -1, $+i$ and $-i$. If z describes a closed curve around any one branch-point w changes sign. Equally, if three branch-points are enclosed; but for two or four branch-points the sign does not change. The point z thus moves from the upper sheet to the lower sheet only if an odd number of branch-points are surrounded.

We must make cuts between the branch-points so that the transition from one sheet to another agrees with our conclusions. We shall not allow the cuts to intersect, for if they did intersect it would be impossible for a curve surrounding two branch-points to lie entirely on one sheet. Therefore, the most obvious choice of cuts would be either between 1 and i and -1 and $-i$, or between 1 and $-i$ and -1 and i (Fig. 204). One could, instead, make cuts between 1 and -1 and i and $-i$, in this case, however, one of the cuts must

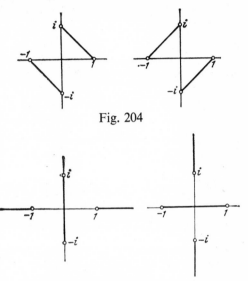

Fig. 204

Fig. 205

go to infinity (Fig. 205) in the plane representation of the points (not of course, in the projection on to a sphere). We shall take the situation in which the cuts are 1, i and -1, $-i$.

We shall determine the connectivity of this Riemann surface, which, like the earlier ones considered, is two-sided. Does every regressive cut divide the surface into two pieces? That there are regressive cuts which do divide it into two pieces is obvious; Fig. 202 shows an example of such a cut. But we shall at once give an example of a regressive cut which does not divide the surface. In Fig. 206 a closed curve surrounds two branch-points. To show that the cut along this curve does not remove a piece of the Riemann surface, it is sufficient to show that one can go on the surface from a point z_1 in the interior of the closed curve to a point z_2 outside it. Assume that the curve lies in the upper sheet. Starting at z_1 in the interior of the curve one can cross over the cut 1, i on to the lower sheet and then cross over the cut 1, $-i$ back up on to the upper sheet. In this way one can get to any point outside the curve in the upper sheet, and clearly even more easily to any point on the lower sheet. Again, a

164 THE TOPOLOGY OF SURFACES

regressive cut which runs from a point on the upper sheet across a branch-cut into the lower sheet, and then across the second branch-cut back into the upper sheet, does not divide the Riemann surface, as is easily verified (Fig. 207).

If we now combine the two cuts (Fig. 208), the surface becomes

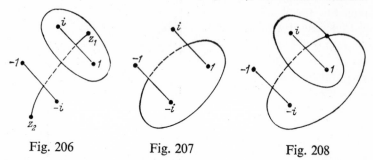

Fig. 206   Fig. 207   Fig. 208

simply connected, being divided into two pieces by any further regressive cut. Hence, the connectivity is

$$z = 3.$$

Take the diagram of Fig. 208 as a polygonal net from which to determine the value of the invariant

$$I = e - k + f$$

of Euler's theorem. Then $e = 1, k = 2, f = 1$, whence

$$I = z - 3 = 0;$$

whence we again have $z = 3$. Since the relationship between connectivity z and genus g is given by

$$z = 2g + 1,$$

it follows that our Riemann surface has genus

$$g = 1,$$

and hence it is topologically equivalent to the torus.

In order to transform the Riemann surface into the torus we shall cut the surface up and rejoin the pieces, taking care that the pieces are correctly connected. Consider the arrangement of cuts[1] exhibited in Fig. 209. The first regressive cut runs from the point i on the upper sheet to the point -1, and from there on the lower sheet back to i. The second regressive cut runs from $+1$ on the upper sheet

[1] *Tr.* The branch cuts are now those on the left in Fig. 205.

via infinity (or, on the equivalent sphere, round the back) to -1, and then, still on the upper sheet, back the same way to the point $+1$, as shown in Fig. 209. This avoids the intersection of cuts. The Riemann surface is now simply connected and so the third regressive cut, which we now add, will divide it into pieces. The last cut runs from the point $+1$ to the point $-i$ on the upper sheet, and back to $+1$ on the lower sheet. We now have the following regions: the

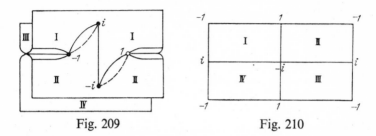

Fig. 209   Fig. 210

upper half of the upper sheet labelled I, the lower half of the upper sheet labelled II, the upper half of the lower sheet labelled III and the lower half of the lower sheet labelled IV. We can deform all four regions topologically into congruent rectangles. Then rectangle I has sides $(i, -i)$, $(-i, 1)$, $(1, -1)$, $(-1, i)$; II has sides $(i, -i)$, $(-i, 1)$, $(1, -1)$, $(-1, i)$; III has sides $(i, -i)$, $(-i, 1)$, $(1, -1)$, $(-1, i)$; IV has sides $(i, -i)$, $(-i, 1)$, $(1, -1)$, $(-1, i)$. It should be noted that if the orientation of each rectangle is given by $i \rightarrow -i$, then rectangles I and III have a positive orientation, II and III a negative orientation. The regions are now joined together as shown in Fig. 210. Then the upper and lower edges of the rectangle are identical and equally the right and left side. If these pairs of sides are joined up we get a torus. This then, discounting the intermediate figures, is equivalent to our Riemann surface.

4. *The Slit-open Sphere of Two Sheets*

At the end of our discussion of the function $w = z + \dfrac{1}{z}$, we examined the slit sphere of two sheets, which using a stereographic projection had been shown to be equivalent to the two-sheeted image plane corresponding to the function. Corresponding to the function $w = \pm \sqrt{z^4 - 1}$ we have a two-sheeted sphere with two slits. We shall try to turn this surface directly into the paradigm of surfaces of connectivity 3 and genus 1, i.e. the torus, or the sphere with one handle.

Label the two branch-cuts on the sphere V and W. If we actually

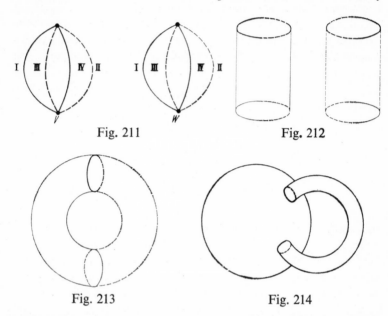

Fig. 211

Fig. 212

Fig. 213

Fig. 214

perform the cuts, then in both cases the surface regions are bounded by four lines; we label these $V_I, V_{II}, V_{III}, V_{IV}$, and $W_I, W_{II}, W_{III}, W_{IV}$, where I refers to the left upper sheet, II to the right upper sheet, III the left lower sheet and IV the right lower sheet. In each case I is to be joined to IV and II to III. Now suppose the slits distended to form holes (Fig. 211); we can then pull the lower sheet out and so obtain two spheres each with two holes. The sphere corresponding to the upper sheet has one hole bounded by V_I and V_{II}, and the other hole bounded by W_I and W_{II}; it can be deformed into a tube. Similarly the sphere corresponding to the lower sheet can be deformed into a tube, the two holes being bounded by V_{III}, V_{IV} and W_{III}, W_{IV}. The two tubes are drawn schematically in Fig. 212. They have to be joined up in such a way that the previously connected lines are properly identified. This gives a torus (Fig. 213) or, if we leave one of the tubes in the form of the original sphere with two holes, and then fit the other tube into the two holes, a sphere with a handle (Fig. 214). In this way we obtain the paradigm of surfaces with connectivity 3 and genus 1.

We can extend this method. Suppose that corresponding to a function we have a Riemann surface of two sheets with three branch-cuts U, V and W and hence six branch-points. Project this surface on to a sphere and replace the branch-cuts by holes, noting which of the 3×4 bounding lines are to be reconnected. Now separate the two sheets of the sphere and deform each sheet into a surface of the form shown in Fig. 215. We can then join the two surfaces as shown in Fig. 216 and the original connections will be re-established. This surface can also be topologically deformed into a sphere with two handles (Fig. 217). It has connectivity $z = 5$ and genus 2. It is obvious that this process can be further generalised.

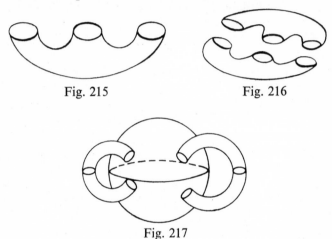

Fig. 215   Fig. 216

Fig. 217

POSTSCRIPT

SOMEBODY ONCE made a statistical investigation of the mathematical papers which appeared throughout the world. He wished to find out which branches of mathematics had proved most fruitful in the last decades. It turned out that topology, which at the turn of the century had lain well back, pushed more and more to the fore and now belonged to the vanguard. As usually happens, combined with this increasing expansion of topological research, the methods were made progressively more theoretical. In this respect two main streams can be distinguished.

Set theoretical topology as expressed, for instance, in the work of HAUSDORFF, developed with the strong forward thrust of set theory created by GEORG CANTOR. The topological structures are represented as point sets.

On the other hand combinatorial or algebraic topology builds topological structures from simplexes, i.e. from line-segments, triangles, tetrahedra, according to the number of dimensions. This method has its origin in the theory of polygons and polyhedra, but extends to any dimension. The elements are described in arithmetical or algebraic terms, so that they are made independent of their geometrical originals and can be applied to other structures.

The modern trend is to unite these two streams. In consequence there are significant problems, such as the proof of the invariance of the concept of dimension which, because of the results of set theory, have become acute. Numerous problems await solution in this attempt to unite these two directions of topological research.

What has been presented in this book may, from the point of view of recent work, be regarded as belonging to a pre-science stage. A leading topologist once referred to these topics as 'curiosa'. Nevertheless, it seems safe to say that a visual introduction to topology is no outrage against the majesty of mathematics, since one no less than DAVID HILBERT included it in his *Anschauliche Geometrie*. But besides this I believe in a sort of genetic law of science. In many other branches of mathematics we come across such developments which have their origins in 'curiosa'; in elementary geometry, in analytic and projective geometry, in the infinitesimal calculus (analysis), in group theory, perhaps to a greater or a lesser extent in all branches of our knowledge. Theory, just as research, may do well to trace its path from the beginnings.

BIBLIOGRAPHY

Tr. In the original bibliography by the author there are nine books all in German. Of these the major works are:

1. P. ALEXANDROFF and H. HOPF, *Topologie*, vol. 1 (Springer, Berlin), 1935.

2. D. HILBERT and S. COHN-VOSSEN, *Anschauliche Geometrie* (Springer, Berlin), 1932.

3. K. REIDEMEISTER, *Einführung in der kombinatorische Topologie* (*Die Wissenschaft*, vol. 86) (Vieweg, Braunschweig), Neudruck, 1950.

The second book has appeared in English under the title *Geometry and the Imagination* (Chelsea, New York), 1952. Another book mentioned by the author which is available in English is the Dover paperback: P. ALEXANDROFF, *Elementary Concepts of Topology*.

There are today more and more books appearing on all aspects of topology. Of the more recent we mention two:

1. B. H. ARNOLD, *Intuitive Concepts in Elementary Topology* (Prentice-Hall), 1963.

2. M. J. MANSFIELD, *Introduction to Topology* (Van Nostrand), 1963.